the autonomous house

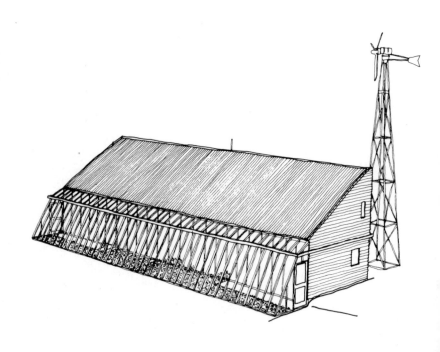

BRENDA AND ROBERT VALE

the autonomous house
DESIGN AND PLANNING FOR
SELF-SUFFICIENCY

THAMES AND HUDSON · LONDON

First published in Great Britain in 1975
Reprinted in 1975, 1976 and 1977

Printed in Great Britain by Unwin Brothers Limited,
The Gresham Press, Old Woking, Surrey

Contents

1 What is an autonomous house?

The autonomous house on its site is defined as a house operating independently of any inputs except those of its immediate environment. The house is not linked to the mains services of gas, water, electricity or drainage, but instead uses the income-energy sources of sun, wind and rain to service itself and process its own wastes. In some ways it resembles a land-based space station which is designed to provide an environment suitable for life but unconnected with the existing life-support structure of Earth. The autonomous house uses the life-giving properties of the Earth but in so doing provides an environment for the occupants without interfering with or altering these properties.

Although the self-serviced house provides a useful starting-point for experiments in autonomy, as it forms a small unit that can be designed, built and tested within a relatively short time, the idea can be expanded to include self-sufficiency in food, the use of on-site materials for building and the reduction of the building and servicing technology to a level where the techniques can be understood and equipment repaired by a person without recourse to specialized training. Although it is possible to survive with pre-industrial technology, this is not what is proposed by autonomous living. At present, however, technology appears to be exploited for its own sake, without thought to its benefits, uses or effects on people or the external environment. We are persuaded to expect a higher material standard of living when, for the majority, the standard that we already have in the West is perfectly adequate. A marginal increase in this standard can only be made with the use of yet greater quantities of the existing resources of the Earth. What are essentials for the American way of life (full central heating, air conditioning, a car per person) are considered, albeit less so now, as luxuries for Europeans, and what are considered necessary for a satisfactory European life (enough to eat, a home and fuel to heat it, access to transport) would be luxuries for the 'third world'. If we cannot find a way of levelling standards rationally while there is time left to consider the problem, then the levelling may be forced on us as the lack of fossil fuels on which western economy so critically depends precipitates a collapse which must change our way of living if we are to survive at all.

The autonomous house is not seen as a regressive step. It is not simply a romantic vision of 'back to the land', with life again assuming a rural pace and every man dependent upon himself and his immediate environment for survival. Rather, it is a different direction for society to take. Instead of growth, stability is the aim; instead of working to earn money to pay other people to keep him alive, the individual is presented with the choice of self-autonomy or working to pay for survival. No such choice exists at present. 'Dropping out' now is a game for those with private means.

Stability would be an obvious goal were it not for the fact that society is so geared to growth in every sense. A stable population, making only what it actually needs, with each article being considered with regard to the material it is made of and what is to be done with it once its useful life is over, and finding all its power from what can be grown or from the sun, would give man back a true place in the world's system. However, a consumer society can exist only by living off the capital resources of the Earth, whether the stored fuels or the reserves of oxygen for running the machinery of the growth economy; and, as has frequently been shown, these reserves are not infinite. The oil shortage in 1974 gave a taste of enforced 'no growth' economy, and our survival at whatever price or hardship will be a first lesson in stability. Whether this lesson will provide the impetus for yet more growth from a nuclear-based economy, or whether it could form the basis of a more rational society, remains to be seen. The autonomous house would only form a very small part of this total picture, but it is an object that can be grasped and realized in material terms at present.

However, the attractive idea of a house generating its own power and recycling its own wastes is almost as difficult to realize as the idea of a stable economy. Apart from the physical limitations of income-energy sources, the system can be made only marginally competitive with existing methods of servicing houses. This difficulty could be removed if autonomy did not have to fit within the present system. At the moment, however, with houses already more expensive than most people can afford, the idea of an increased capital cost for houses, even though future running costs would be reduced, could never be accepted.

The idea of autonomy probably arose from two quests. The first was to gain free power for house heating, etc., so that conventional fuels need not be bought, and the second was to free the planning of communities. At present any new building must link to an existing or purpose-built service network. Cities, therefore, expand around their edges in order to keep houses on the mains, although expansion is limited by the size of the existing servicing plants. Removal of this restraint would enable houses to be built virtually anywhere, and communities would be formed for a more logical reason than the need to be fed and watered at a central point. Existing cities can be likened to babies in that they are serviced completely from the outside and the control of their functions is at the will of a very few people. If any one person declares a state of emergency, half a million people may sit in the dark unable to help themselves. Autonomy could provide for every community to become adult. Each person or community would be in control of his own heating, lighting, food production, etc. A real decentralization of control would be achieved and every person would become self-governing.

Even if the implications of autonomy can never be accepted, the concept itself has certain essential properties which might help to alleviate the impending fuel crisis. In the 1950s and earlier, many books were written to demonstrate the finite limits of available fossil fuels, and many of these statistics have been taken up and used as the basis of the 1972-73 'doom debate'. No two authorities agree on the actual limits to the fossil fuels remaining but, given the present energy consumption and accepting the trends for increased demand in the future, it seems that reserves of natural gas and oil will be exhausted in the next fifty to seventy-five years, while the coal reserves might last for 350 years. However, as has already happened, political pressures can easily upset these predictions to precipitate an energy crisis much earlier. Given the present economic system, as the reserves dwindle and the demand for the product increases, it becomes more valuable. It therefore pays to leave commodities such as oil in the ground and become richer without effort. The price of the oil then automatically inflates, given the artificial shortage and the demand. Such a deadlock is broken only if alternative fuels can be found to reduce the demand for oil and hence its value.

Alternative sources of energy have therefore been sought in order to maintain the status quo. The sources that were used by man in the past seem unattractive, not intrinsically, but because of the vast populations that they must be made to serve. Wood, with about half the calorific. value of coal, can easily be burnt directly for space and water heating, used to fire boilers for steam and even processed into a motor fuel, as was common in Sweden during the last war; it can also regenerate itself every hundred years. Wood has many of the properties required of a fuel for our present society, especially as different varieties can be grown successfully all over the world. But man has already reduced the forests of the world by 30 per cent in order to free more land for agriculture, and with the coming difficulties of feeding the predicted population of the world in AD 2000, it would be impossible to grow wood to service it as well.

As forestry becomes less attractive, attention has turned to resources that make more efficient use of the available land. All plant life represents a conversion of solar energy falling on the plant into a certain mass of biological material. A forest is a low converter of incident energy into bio-mass, for a typical pine forest will produce 10 tonnes per hectare per year, rising to 59 T/ha/year for a tropical rain forest. Because of this emphasis on conversion, it has been suggested that algae might be grown under artificial conditions whereby yields of up to 86 T/ha/year might be obtained. Processes have been outlined for the conversion of these algae into recognizable fuels such as methane, or hydrocarbons similar to petrol. However, the over-all efficiencies of such systems are very low, being about 13 kilowatts per hectare, compared to an actual solar incidence of about 7000 kW/ha.

There are one or two odd sources of biological fuel which might be considered. A managed peat bog, for instance, can produce a consistent supply of fuel as it regenerates every hundred years or more, although it is extremely limited in quantity on a global scale and its present exploitation is very localized. In under-developed countries dried cakes of farm dung have been used to a significant extent for cooking the daily meal and for space heating, but rather than viewing this as an exploitable fuel, the practice would be better eliminated. Not only does the irritating smoke cause eye disease, but the land suffers when deprived of the manure. For this reason low-cost methods have been devised in India and elsewhere for decomposing manure to give methane as a fuel to replace the dried dung, and a composted slurry which enriches the soil. Since the present energy demands in the 'third world' are so low, such a system of energy supply is satisfactory.

For more exigent life-styles a direct conversion of solar energy into useful heat seems preferable to the growth of bio-mass for fuel competing with the growth of bio-mass for food in an over-populated world. It seems very unlikely, however, that solar energy could be used as an alternative for fuelling our present society. Disregarding the vast cost that would be incurred, solar electric power stations could not provide a more efficient source of energy than the present system. The present over-all conversion of fossil fuels to electricity in a conventional power station is about 20 per cent of the theoretical maximum once transmission losses have been taken into account, and it is unlikely that a solar power station would improve on this. At the same time, the problems of conventional transmission present defined limits, so that it would be impossible to build a great number of solar power stations along the equator and other areas of maximum sun, and then transport the power to where it is required. Very low transmission losses could theoretically be achieved by using low-temperature techniques, but this would require more energy to maintain the temperature involved, which would further reduce the efficiency of the system and increase the area of solar collectors required. It was claimed that a plot of land equal in area to two-fifths of the state of New Mexico covered with tracking mirrors could supply the energy required for power and industry in the USA in 1950. Not only would such an installation be inadequate to meet the 1975 demands, but the problem of storing vast quantities of power for times when the sun was not shining would have to be solved, as would also the problem of transmitting power from New Mexico to the industrial complexes, four or five times as far as it is possible at present. Unless all these problems can be solved, the use of solar energy will have to be decentralized and restricted to domestic house space and water heating and similar uses.

A small portion of the solar energy falling on the earth is used to drive the atmospheric and oceanic currents around the globe, the energy eventually being dissipated into heat by friction. Wind power, even though it is distributed over a wide area, like solar energy, has in the past been exploited at a scale large enough to generate power for the grid. The chosen sites were very windy, as at the site of the ERA generator in the Orkneys, the most powerful wind regimes being in the latitudes between 40° and 55°. Standing 23 m high, the ERA unit was designed to feed 400,000 kilowatt-hours a year into the neighbouring 11kV grid. Thus for any useful generation of power, windmills have to be very large and again located in depopulated windy areas. Where transmission losses can be virtually eliminated by placing a windmill next to the house, it is possible to generate a small quantity of electricity with a much smaller mill, but the electricity thus produced would at present cost more than that generated in the central plant.

Hydro-electric power, which is in turn derived from the evaporation of water from the sea and land masses by the sun, does provide a central-ized source of electricity independent of fossil fuels. Although the quantities of water flowing through rivers are vast, the number of suitable sites where water can be impounded with a considerable head are very small, and many have already been exploited. Of the available sites, most are situated in the 'third world', where the demand for power is less and where the technological facilities for development of sites on a large scale are lacking. Even when built, dams and reservoirs can have a comparatively short life, as, where it occurs, silting slowly reduces their efficiency and finally chokes them completely. Excluding the problems of plant location, the total hydro-electric production would be quite inadequate when compared to total energy demands.

Other sources of power which, like hydro-electricity, are restricted in location and number include geothermal power (using the heat beneath the earth's crust) and tidal power. Both methods of power generation have been exploited, the geothermal in Iceland and at Larderello in Italy, and the tidal at a station at Rance, France, but both are limited in the sites available and the power that can be produced from them.

This very brief survey of alternative energy sources has not produced any alternative to oil which can be so easily distributed over a wide area. Sites exploiting natural power sources are disparate and distant from existing industrial locations, and income-energy sources of solar and wind power could only be used to supply a very reduced demand. However, one panacea has been offered to mankind in the form of nuclear energy. The present oil crisis will doubtless precipitate a rash of nuclear power stations over America and Europe, no longer thought uneconomic when compared with conventional oil- and coal-burning stations, and we shall all exist in electrically-heated houses, with steam-driven machinery for industry and hydrogen-powered cars. The energy crisis will have been solved.

However, even nuclear science is having trouble in keeping up with the present demand for energy. The earliest nuclear power stations were only 30 per cent efficient in the generation of electricity from the fission of uranium, compared with 50 per cent for the best coal-fired stations. At the same time ores of suitable uranium were limited, and it was realized that the predicted world requirements for the next ten years, assuming that oil was not withheld by the Arabs, could only be supplied by using more than half of the total uranium reserves. For this reason breeder reactors have been developed, in which more nuclear fuel is actually produced in the reactor than is consumed. An experimental reactor of this type has been operating at Dounreay in Scotland since 1959. The reactor breeds plutonium in the 'blanket' of uranium around the fuel charge and the product can be used as the fuel of fast reactors to breed still more plutonium.

It was hoped that this type of reactor would be built in Britain from the late 1970s, although the dangers of plutonium and the difficulties of handling it have made research into the safety and security of the reactors very necessary. The thermal reactors already in use and the fast breeder reactors, as well as producing vast quantities of power, also produce radioactive waste, and this probably poses more of a threat to the nuclear programme than the dangers of plutonium and the chances of it being stolen for home-made atomic warheads. The nuclear waste will become an inheritance of many generations to come. Some of it has to be maintained in specialized conditions, as at Windscale, Cumberland, where a quantity of radioactive waste equal in volume to a semi-detached house must be refrigerated for tens of thousands of years. The UK Atomic Energy Authority state that 'by the year 2000 Britain will obtain over 75 per cent of her electricity supplies from nuclear power', but whether the dangers in such nuclear exploitation are worth the energy thus gained is a problem that must be resolved. The fact that some nuclear scientists are worried about the position may be a guide. However, if society demands energy, then the government will promise to provide it, whatever the cost to future generations. There will perhaps be one or two nuclear accidents, but no doubt scientists will be found to say that the level of radiation in the environment can be increased without any real harm to the population. Governments will play down the dangers of radiation and will persuade us that an increased chance of contracting leukaemia is a small price to pay to achieve the better standard of living offered by abundant power from the 'peaceful atom'. In fact no radiation is safe. At present we are exposed to radiation from cosmic rays and from granitic rocks which contain small amounts of naturally radioactive substances. We have the choice of living in an area of higher or lower background radiation. If successive governments, fearful of the consequences of interrupting growth, continue to increase the number of nuclear power stations, we shall all be exposed to increasing levels of radiation and shall not be able to move away if we wish to.

One other possibility remains, that of nuclear fusion rather than fission. The enormous amounts of energy radiated from the sun and stars are produced by the fusion of hydrogen isotopes into helium, and this fusion has already been achieved in the laboratory in an un-controlled form. Deuterium, the isotope of hydrogen which has the greatest potential for fusion power, exists in sea water, 28 cubic kilometres of sea water containing enough deuterium to produce power equivalent to the world's ultimate coal resources. The end products of a controlled fusion reaction are mainly harmless helium, and this fact, coupled with the relative abundance of the raw materials compared with the known resources of uranium, have made fusion a dream power of the future, but one whose exploitation is not immediately fore-seeable. We have to survive at least the first generation of fast breeder reactors before fusion power can be sufficiently developed.

In addition to the hidden dangers of nuclear power, a further nuclear disaster is impending. As the western standard of living is threatened, there is an increased likelihood of war being used as a method of gaining the necessary resources. While governments continue to promise limitless benefits to their countries, methods must be found of supplying these, otherwise governments become unpopular and are ousted by their rivals. However, the lack of fuel will itself alter the pattern of warfare, and the temptation to channel all resources into dropping one large warhead may be hard to resist when the alternative is cavalry and bicycle troops. (*Jane's Weapon Systems*, an authoritative manual of world armaments, has suggested this in the introduction to the 1973-74 volume.) Thus one or other nuclear disaster threatens the species of man unless rational alternatives can be found.

Whether we can ever lower our standard of living depends upon acceptance of the fact that there is a definable standard attainable by all alike. At the minute we are living on the earth's capital, so that the actual time spent on survival by each person has been reduced. Even in the 'third world', where farming societies prevail, the so-called aid from richer countries has altered the previously stable society. 'Interference' has lowered the infant mortality rate and made for longer lives so that the land can no longer support the people on it. Disease and famine then occur and once again help must be put in to bail out the unstable population. While it cannot be argued that reducing infant mortality is bad, if done in isolation its effect may not be entirely beneficial. Some western countries, including Britain, are already so overpopulated that if the 'aid', in the shape of capital resources and energy, were to be removed, the land could not support the people on it, and as disease and famine followed there would be no friendly agency to offer help.

It may therefore be best to define a standard of living that could be achieved by every person on Earth, taking into account the amount of income energy, finite resources and land and sea available for cultivation. The standard would thus depend on the population level agreed upon, given the fact that finite resources are incompatible with an infinite population. Whether it is possible to organize such a standard on a world basis is very questionable. It may be that each country will have to achieve stability within itself, and then the temptation to encroach on someone else's resources may become overwhelming to the point of warfare. However, were such a national autonomy to be achieved, each country would then stabilize itself around a certain population enjoying enough food, heat, light and care to remain healthy, and enough time and leisure to feel fulfilled.

Any imposition of limits dismisses entirely the theory that 'technology will muddle through'. It refuses to accept that nuclear energy will supply us with unlimited power; soya beans and algae with unlimited food; the galaxy with unlimited planets to colonize and mine; and mankind with unlimited inventiveness to solve our problems. It accepts that there is a useful limit to technology. That is not to say that solutions and advances cannot be imagined, but that we should have the wisdom to choose to

14

build what is useful to mankind. In some respects these limits are being reached; the immediate planets have failed to yield anything but a rather hostile environment and a quantity of dust. America seems to have finished its space programme before the end of the twentieth century. It already seems that a useful limit to space travel has been reached. There will be no more men on the moon as there is no point to their going – truly the end of a vision.

At a more mundane level, consider the history of the gramophone. When Edison invented the phonograph, a visible step forward was obvious, as sound could now be recorded and reproduced. The original phonograph was later replaced by the gramophone, with double-sided disc records to replace the fragile wax cylinders. Later, electric motors replaced the earlier clockwork gramophone motors, which saved winding. Long-playing plastic records were a big advance on the 78 r.p.m. shellac discs. Then came high-fidelity reproduction of sound followed by stereo reproduction, and the difference, although not so noticeable as that between the electric gramophone and the high-fidelity system, could still be perceived. Now we have 'quadraphonic' sound, although we still have only two ears. By now the difference can barely be heard but has to be measured electrically. The human ear has set a limit on the reproduction of sound.

Lighting levels in American schools provide another example. Before 1910 the recommended level was 32 lux (lumen/m^2). This was raised to 194 lux between 1910 and 1930, and after 1930 to 323 lux. Since 1950, levels have risen to between 753 and 1613 lux. In fact 323 lux is sufficient to come within 7 per cent of the theoretical limit of the human eye, and a level of 1613 lux will give only a further 3-4 per cent increase in this performance. The very high levels have now been reduced as it was realized that the practical limit had been reached and passed. These two examples show a limit to standards set by the human body. Acceptance of the fact that technology is limited in its usefulness opposes the legend of the superiority of man perpetually driving him to improve on his standard of living. However, if we do not choose to restrict technology now, the fact that our technology is based on fuels of finite amount may restrict it without our consent in the future.

Autonomy in housing, rather than autonomy for countries, is an idea that comes from the distribution of income energies. Apart from specialized cases of hydro-electric or geothermal power, solar and wind energy, together with timber, are distributed evenly over the surface of the Earth. The logic of the situation is therefore to place the house as a free-standing unit in the middle of its plot where it can use directly the energy falling on it. Once the house becomes decentralized then other systems follow. The house would be surrounded by a plot large enough for the occupants to grow their food and become even more self-sufficient. The large plot can in fact become an integral part of the servicing system when the generation of methane gas is considered.

From this emerges a picture of a stable, decentralized society where each person is directly responsible for most of his survival. This vision of having to work the land and operate the house in a rural utopia immediately brings feelings of horror to most people. But, given ambient energy sources, no other future seems possible. Arguments have been made for centralized ambient services such as methane generation on a large scale, but even central services serving the city require methods of collecting and transporting the materials to the plant. This proposition might become a possibility with very high-density cities where transportation of raw materials and energy could be minimized. However, if the demand for existing fuels could be reduced, it might be possible to offer a greater choice of living standards and patterns than at the moment.

New housing could be built in a decentralized way, with plots for food-growing. The people on this land would then grow their own food at a higher productivity rate than in conventional chemical farming, and at the same time the houses would service themselves. However, such buildings would have increased capital costs with regard to both the land and the extra plant supplied with the house. Alternatively, high-density living could be supplied as in existing cities, where people work to make the reduced quantities of goods required by a more self-sufficient economy, and pay for the food and energy they use within this city. Such energy might come from the resources we use now, such as coal, or from centralized income sources such as methane or wind.

The middle stratum would be the present suburbs, which could be partly autonomized to run on a reduced energy supply. People living here could both work in society and practise a degree of autonomy. Large inter-war gardens could be made productive; better insulation would reduce energy demands, and some income energy might also be employed. Such a situation could provide a transition between new autonomous housing and the decentralized society based on village groupings, and the present stock of existing high-energy level housing.

A real choice would then exist between different ways of living: in existing cities, where one would work and pay for other people to provide one's services, a small service industry being necessary for each city; in a zone of housing partly converted to autonomy where people would have to work and pay for some additional energy and food; or in an area of new housing where self-sufficiency could be practised. The agricultural land around cities could continue to be used to supply existing cities and towns, and land further away, unsuitable for traditional agriculture, might be used for small, high-productivity family plots. This would present a real choice in ways of living. At present we have no choice. One must work to earn money to buy food. As the price of food rises so one must work more to earn more. There is no choice in the air we breathe; if other people choose to pollute it by building motorways and thereby generating traffic to put toxic fumes into the atmosphere, then there is nothing we can do but breathe it. With centralized services in the hands of the few, a small disruption can affect a great many people, and there is no choice in whether one is affected or not.

How desirable such decentralization is in political terms, with removal of choice from the few to the many, is open to discussion. An autonomous country would mean one where there would be no growth in the economy, where population size was strictly controlled, where a higher standard of living could not be expected, where resources were shared equally between every man, where freedom to act was curtailed by the need to survive. The society would be unlike any that we know at the moment. It would encompass something of many previous political doctrines but it would be aimed at providing for the survival of mankind, given that our present method of living off capital cannot go on for all time.

Any acceptance of the desirability of autonomy can only be based on faith. If you believe that it is important for man to be part of his natural ecology, to know how survival is accomplished, to be in control of his own life, then autonomy is a logical outcome. If, however, you believe that mankind has always solved every problem that arises, that eventually some way will be found for dealing with nuclear waste after a given number of years of research, and that the benefits of cheap nuclear power outweigh the possible dangers, then there is no case for autonomy and the status quo will be maintained.

If you take the step, decide that things will only become worse, and therefore decide to attempt self-sufficiency in food and energy, then the house provides a convenient starting-point. It is easier to say that centralized services can still be provided with income-energy sources, but it would take a great deal of money to carry out such an experiment. However, it is still possible to find rural areas where one can attempt self-sufficiency in fuel and experiment with autonomy in housing. If forced to convert an existing house rather than designing and building a new experimental one, it may be that only partial autonomy can be achieved and small amounts of fossil fuels might be burnt to supplement income-energy sources over the coldest parts of the year. However, even this type of experiment will provide new information by putting some

17

of the theories and ideas into practice. Even if the house is found to be on the wrong scale for exploiting income-energy sources, the experiment will, we hope, have shown that the ideas are practical.

One live, working experiment, however impractical if it were applied universally, will transmit an idea far better than a shelf full of theoretical reports. Something that can be seen and touched and shown to work to some degree arouses curiosity, and curiosity in turn leads to solutions. This is why the following chapters relate income-energy sources and food production directly to one house, since this is the easiest unit to actually establish. The success or failure of the autonomous experiments that will probably be set up in the next few years may be important for the survival of mankind.

2 Power from the sun

Plants have been artificially heated by the sun in specially designed environments for many years, but although the heating effect of sunlight entering buildings through glass windows has been recognized and even designed for, the idea of totally heating a house by the sun's energy entering it and falling upon it has only recently been exploited. Both systems require the use of a material that will effectively trap the incoming radiation, and glass has been the only material to fulfil this purpose for many years. Recently, however, transparent plastics having similar properties have been developed. Because the discovery of methods of manufacturing cast glass in the late eighteenth century coincided with the establishment of a nationwide transport system, glass became a much cheaper and more widely available material. In conjunction with cast-iron members, the Victorians exploited its properties as a waterproof cladding material that allowed daylight and sunlight within the structure. Even earlier, its value as a material for trapping solar energy had been used, by those who could afford it, for building forcing houses for out-of-season fruit and vegetables. Such was the fascination of this phenomenon for gardeners and designers that a sophisticated science developed around the need to optimize the shape of the glasshouses in order to obtain the correct temperatures and conditions for the delicate plants inside.

When sunlight falls on a sheet of glass the majority of the energy passes directly through, while some is reflected and some absorbed by the glass. The energy absorbed by the glass raises its temperature and is re-radiated by the glass both to the inside and the outside (see fig. 1).

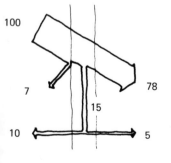

1 The percentages of solar radiation passing through clear glass (after Rouvier, 1973). 7 per cent of the incoming radiation is reflected, 78 per cent passes directly through to the inside and 15 per cent is absorbed by the glass. Of this, 10 per cent is re-radiated to the outside and 5 per cent to the inside. The percentage reflected will depend upon the angle of incidence of the solar radiation.

The energy that passes through the glass is absorbed by the plants in a greenhouse or by the walls, furniture and floor within a room, thus raising their temperature. This absorbed heat is then redistributed, partly by conduction into the object itself, partly by convection and partly by re-radiation to surfaces at a lower temperature, such as the windows and walls not directly lit. However, glass, although transparent to short-wave solar radiation, is opaque to the longer-wave radiation emitted by the objects or plants and hence the radiation is trapped within the enclosure and the temperature rises (fig. 2).

To obtain adequate temperatures within a greenhouse in winter or early spring, the portion of sunlight passing through the glass must be as great as possible. For this reason, the first method devised for tempering the environment centred upon the correct angle for the glass to make with the horizontal, so that the amount of sunlight reflected was minimized. Since ambient summer temperatures are high enough so that additional heating for unspecialized greenhouses is unnecessary,

2   *The greenhouse effect. Glass is transparent to energy of wavelength 0.4–2.5 microns and thus allows the radiant energy of the sun (0.4–0.8 microns) to pass through. The energy is then absorbed by the plants and, although some of the absorbed heat is lost by conduction and convection, the remainder is re-emitted as radiation having a wavelength centring on 11 microns. As glass is opaque at these wavelengths, the radiation is trapped and the temperature inside the greenhouse rises.*

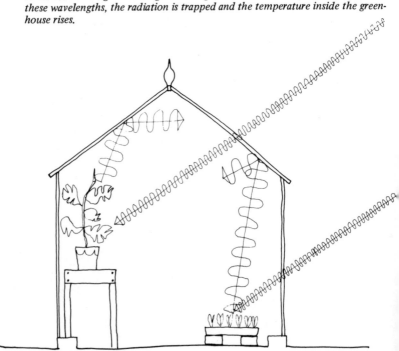

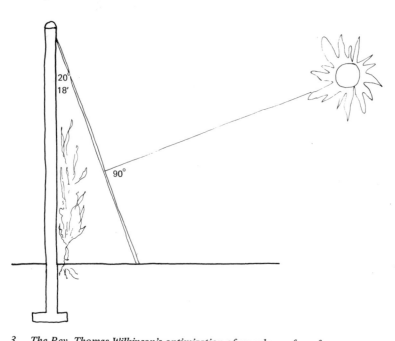

3   *The Rev. Thomas Wilkinson's optimization of greenhouse form for*
February 1st.
Latitude 52° 30'
Complement of latitude = 90° –52° 30' = 37° 30'
Declination for 1 February = –17° 12'
Therefore angle between back wall of house and glass = 20° 18'

the inclination of the glass was optimized for winter. The Rev. Thomas
Wilkinson (Loudon, 1817) put this idea into a formula that could be
used by every gardener to work out an angle for the glass that could be
fitted exactly to the type of greenhouse and the crop grown in it. He
stated that the angle contained between the back wall of the house and
the roof should be made equal to the complement of the latitude
where the greenhouse was to be built, plus or minus the value for the
sun's declination on the actual day when the sun's rays were to fall
perpendicularly (see fig. 3). As with all such optimizations, if the sun
was clouded over on the optimum day it was unfortunate. Nevertheless,
a form for the greenhouse was established to provide optimum
penetration of sunlight in winter. This simple rule survived for many
years until modern mass-production methods, coupled with the use for
greenhouse heating of gas or oil, which eliminate the fumes detrimental
to plants emitted by coal, produced the acres of low-pitched glass
roofs we see today.

    Compared with these modern greenhouses, the Victorian and earlier
forcing houses used simple but sophisticated methods for tempering

21

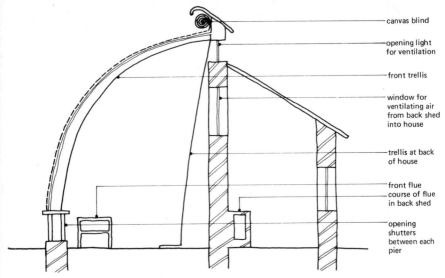

Labels (top to bottom, right side):
- canvas blind
- opening light for ventilation
- front trellis
- window for ventilating air from back shed into house
- trellis at back of house
- front flue
- course of flue in back shed
- opening shutters between each pier

4   *Principles for the construction of hothouses (after Loudon, 1817).*

the environment. As can be seen in fig. 4, the glass forms a lean-to against a solid wall, which in turn has a lean-to shed on the north side. On sunny days this solid wall would absorb some of the incoming solar radiation but, because of its high thermal capacity, a lot of energy would have to be absorbed before the temperature of the wall became high enough for it to re-radiate energy to its surroundings. At night, however, when the surroundings cooled down rapidly as the glass provided little barrier to heat flow, the wall would re-radiate heat to the house and thus help to maintain a more even temperature. This tempering effect was helped if the glass was covered at night with some form of insulation such as a blind or a rush mat. The back shed played an important part in tempering the ventilation air. The forcing houses usually had supplementary heating plants for days when the sun was not shining, and the flue gases from the stove were arranged to pass through the back shed, thus warming the air. The air in the shed then passed through doors in the dividing wall, while stale air was extracted from the greenhouse and ventilated to the outside.

Loudon (1817) made a further innovation in the design of glasshouses to maximize the sun's influence on any type of longitudinal south-facing construction. Instead of running parallel to the slope of the roof, the glazing bars were alternately depressed and raised to form a 'ridge and furrow' pattern. This meant that there were two periods in each day when the sun's rays were perpendicular to some portion of the glass, one before midday and one after, depending upon the angle

22

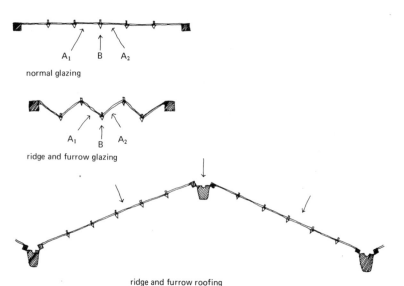

normal glazing

ridge and furrow glazing

ridge and furrow roofing

5   *In ridge and furrow glazing and roofing, the rays of the sun at 11 a.m. (A_1) are perpendicular to one half of the glass; with flat glazing, their angle of incidence is 20°, and 2.5 per cent of the sunlight is reflected. The same situation occurs again at 1 p.m. (A_2). At 12 noon the reflective loss from ridge and furrow glazing is the same as that from flat glazing, with the sun shown at B, but since each ray is at its maximum elevation, so that the glass is receiving maximum power from the sun, the loss is more than balanced by the extra gain at 11 a.m. and 1 p.m. The Great Conservatory at Chatsworth (below), built by Sir Joseph Paxton and Decimus Burton in 1836, employs the principles outlined above.*

of elevation of the ridge and furrow bars. Alternatively, the rafters could be depressed and raised to form ridge and furrow roofing. This method of glazing could be applied equally well to vertical or sloping glass, whether the slope was straight, part circle or some other configuration (see fig. 5).

23

Some simple requirements for solar-heated buildings emerge from the study of glasshouses: a large glass area facing south to trap the solar energy, which is then covered at night with some form of insulation to cut down the heat lost from the house; a solid north-facing wall to cut down the heat loss and also to act as a day-to-day heat store of solar energy, the energy being re-radiated at night; some method of tempering the ventilation air to cut down the heat lost through ventilation with cold air from outside; and optimization of the glass for heat collection in winter when the heat is most needed. Although these sophistications have been dismissed as uneconomic for mass-produced, heated and air-conditioned glass sheds, the principles outlined above will reappear in the considerations of methods for heating houses for people by solar energy.

The greenhouse effect is the basic mechanism for flat-plate solar collectors, which have in turn formed the basis of most solar heating systems for houses. Unlike the greenhouses which were optimized without direct reference to the plants, consumer acceptance has played a large part in the design of most solar-heated buildings. For this reason, most solar heating systems are designed to look and act like normal heating systems, with the boiler replaced by a flat-plate collector.

A flat-plate collector is made of some black sheet, usually metal, covered by one or more sheets of glass or clear plastic. The solar radiation passes through the glass and is absorbed by the black metal which re-radiates the energy as long-wave radiation. As this long-wave radiation cannot pass through the glass, the temperature of the black plate rises. Air or water is then passed over the black sheet where it is heated, and, as long as the sun continues to shine, the temperature of the air or water leaving the collector can be maintained (see figs. 6-8). However, to use the air or water in a conventional heating system, the collector must reach a relatively high temperature. As the collector temperature increases, so does the heat loss from it to the outside air, and it becomes necessary to put two or more layers of glass over the black absorbent surface in order to reduce the heat loss. This in turn reduces the amount of solar radiation that actually reaches the black surface as a higher proportion is now absorbed and reflected by the multiple panes of glass. A balance must therefore be attained. Increasing the number of clear coverings also increases the cost and complexity of the collector and it is usually accepted that solar collectors for most areas of Britain and the USA are double-glazed only.

Unlike plants, which have always been housed in heated or partially heated houses of glass so that maximum daylight can enter for photosynthesis, human beings have traditionally been housed in solid-walled structures with limited openings for daylight and sunlight. Hence, when

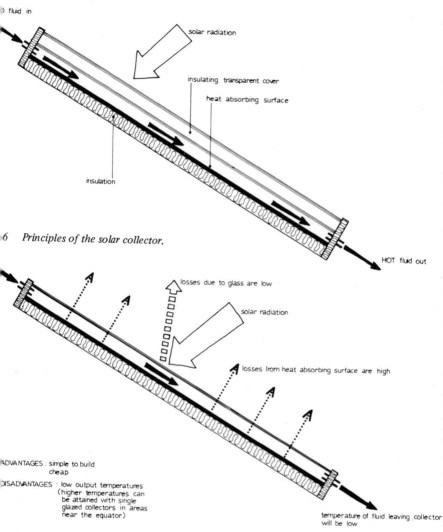

fluid in

solar radiation

insulating transparent cover

heat absorbing surface

insulation

6   *Principles of the solar collector.*

HOT fluid out

losses due to glass are low

solar radiation

losses from heat absorbing surface are high

ADVANTAGES : simple to build
          cheap

DISADVANTAGES : low output temperatures
          (higher temperatures can
          be attained with single
          glazed collectors in areas
          near the equator)

temperature of fluid leaving collector
will be low

7   *Principles of the solar collector: the effect of a single glass cover.*

the problem of solar-heated houses was first studied, traditional house
forms were adapted, rather than using partially solar-heated greenhouse
forms and adapting them for human occupation. Since people have
always welcomed sunshine in their homes, some form of window must
be provided in the south side of the house, and this at once limits the
total space available for direct solar collection with flat-plate collectors.
Although some solar heating effect is produced by the placing of
windows in the east-, south- or west-facing walls, some other reasonably

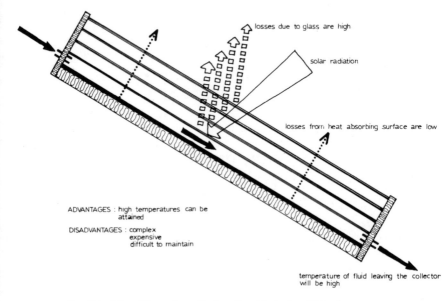

losses due to glass are high

solar radiation

losses from heat absorbing surface are low

ADVANTAGES : high temperatures can be attained

DISADVANTAGES : complex
expensive
difficult to maintain

temperature of fluid leaving the collector
will be high

8 Principles of the solar collector: the effect of multiple glass covers.

high-temperature heat source is needed to bring the house up to the comfort conditions that the rapidly spreading use of central heating has brought us to expect. In order to obtain this extra heat, flat-plate collectors must be used for air or water heating by arranging them along the south side of the house, either vertically on the walls or at an angle on the roof. Architectural problems then emerge with the optimization of the slope of the collectors, which is still often assessed by the latitude method of the Rev. Thomas Wilkinson. Dichotomies occur between the necessity for a steeply sloping roof and the limited use that can be made of the space thus described within the building, as well as difficulties with the disposition of collectors and windows along south-facing walls. Such problems can only be evaluated by reducing everything to a cost basis and comparing the cost of the floor space involved with the cost of the extra energy that can be collected (see fig. 9).

Even the estimation of the energy that can be collected from a collector of given area and tilt is difficult. Either the problem is treated in a much simplified but not necessarily accurate way so that some estimation of the magnitude of the energy that can be collected is made, or a more complex analysis of the dynamic situation must be carried out. The former method was used for most of the solar houses described in this chapter, the estimations being compared with experimental results obtained once the design had been built and tested. For

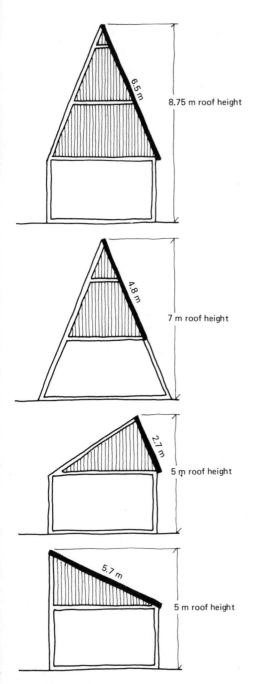

67° collector as part of a conventional roof. The shaded area represents the unused space. Although the collector is optimised for winter collection the roof height is excessive.

8.75 m roof height

6.5 m

A-frame building of equivalent floor area. Here the total optimised collector area is smaller but the unusable space is also reduced.

7 m roof height

4.8 m

67° collector fixed in the normal house height of 5 m. A small optimal collector area is produced.

5 m roof height

2.7 m

30° collector covering all the roof surface. A much larger collector area is produced although the angle is not optimised for winter collection. This larger area will collect more energy than the smaller steeper collector on the same size house in winter and considerably more in summer.

5 m roof height

5.7 m

9   *Some positions for flat-plate collectors (leaving the south wall free).*

a more complex analysis many variables must be brought into consideration. Energy can only be collected once the plate has reached a sufficiently high temperature, and if pumps or fans are used to drive the heat-transfer medium across the black absorber, the energy that can be collected at the lowest possible temperature must be greater than the energy required to operate these pumps or fans. As well as transferring heat to the water or air, heat is lost from the collector by conduction through to the inside of the house, by radiation from the warm collector to the outside air and by convection in the air layer between the plate and the glass covering. The number of covering sheets and their maintenance and degree of degradation in sunlight (if plastic) will also affect the total energy collected over a period. Although it is possible to obtain total daily hours of sunshine from meteorological data, the intermittency of the sunlight is not recorded, and hence the collector may be continually warmed and cooled as clouds pass over the sun. The thermal capacity of the collector and its ability to heat up and cool down quickly must, therefore, also be considered. If the sun shines continuously, the black absorbent surface continues to rise in temperature, and although heated water or air can often be usefully collected at these higher temperatures, the heat loss from the collector, as we have seen, also increases with increasing temperature and hence the over-all efficiency of collection drops (see fig. 10). Thus even though an efficiency can be established for a particular design in a particular location, climatic differences may alter this efficiency if the same collector is constructed somewhere else.

As can be seen, detailed estimates of energy collection are very complicated, and therefore it is usual, for simple installations, to take the tilt of the collector, the required air or water temperature and some assumed conservative efficiency based on other experiments and to use these data, together with the meteorological data available for the site or for somewhere as near the site as possible, to find some estimation of the energy that could be collected (see p. 63). The actual design of the collector is more a matter of cost, availability of materials and ease of construction as, judging from the majority of collectors that have been built, one design seems to work very much the same as another.

Since it has been demonstrated that flat-plate collectors can be incorporated into house designs and heating systems, and even possibly into existing housing stock, to produce at least partial solar heating with a subsequent fuel saving, why are we not already living in solar-heated houses? At present the cost of the solar heating systems is much higher than that of conventional systems, and at a time when house prices have already increased beyond the reach of most people, an increase in the capital cost of houses with the prospect of a future saving in running

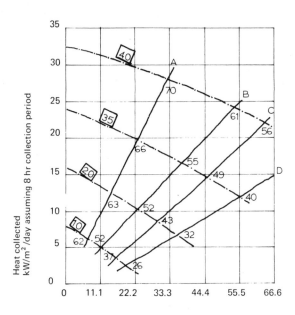

Maximum temperature reached above atmospheric temperature °C

10   Heat collected per day vs. maximum temperature reached (after Heywood, 1954).
— · — · — Incident radiation in kW/m² /day for an 8-hour collection period.
A *represents a collector with 98 kg of water per square metre circulating under pressure from a pump. The hot water is constantly being withdrawn from the system and replaced with cold feed water. Although the maximum temperatures achieved are lower, the efficiency of collection is high. With an incident radiation of 20 kW/m² / day it is possible to collect 12.5 kW of heat per square metres at a temperature of approximately 14° C above atmospheric, at an efficiency of 63 per cent.*
B *represents a collector operating with 49 kg of water per square metre circulating through it by natural thermosiphon action, assuming that all the water reaches the maximum temperature possible (i.e. the temperature at which gains from the collector equal losses) while the sun is shining.*
C *represents the above situation allowing for the more realistic possibility that not all the water will reach the maximum temperature.*
D *represents a situation in which the collector is filled with water to a capacity of 24 kg per square metre and left for the full 8-hour period. Although the possible attainable temperatures are higher, less water reaches the higher temperature, and the efficiency of collection is lower since the heat losses from the collector at a high temperature are greater.*
The figures at the points of intersection represent the percentage efficiency of collection.

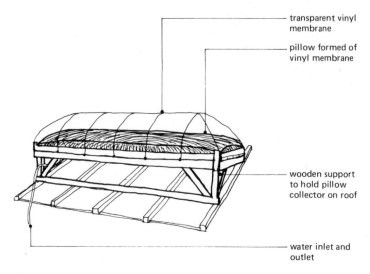

11 Japanese pillow-type collector. These collectors measure approximately 1 m x 2 m and hold about 200 litres. The pillow itself has either the top sheet clear and the bottom sheet black or both surfaces black. The collectors are sold in Japan for between $6 and $12, and last for about two years.

costs will hardly be acceptable. Government approval of the use of solar energy as a new utility might also help its acceptance on a wide scale; this official approval has not always been lacking, as the aim of the Presidential Materials Policy Commission in 1952 was to have, by 1975, some thirteen million houses in the USA, mostly in the southern half, deriving the major part of their heating from the sun. Even if collectors can be incorporated in the structure to form the roof of the building, a collector will cost more than a conventional roof. To the cost of the collector must be added the cost of heat storage, even if the number of pipes and ducts for distributing heat are similar for both solar and conventional systems. The storage must be costed in terms of the materials used, the containers for holding these and the amount of useful floor space it takes up within the building. If the volume of storage is reduced in relation to the collector area so that the system is not capable of taking the full heating load, then some auxiliary heating must be supplied. Even though the boiler might be smaller than for a full central-heating system, the cost is not reduced proportionately. Thus, although theoretically the solar energy for heating the house is free, the capital cost of installing the equipment to maintain comfortable conditions is very high. As fossil fuels have until recently remained cheap, there has been no incentive to invest money for a return only realized in the future.

Simple flat-plate collectors are already in widespread use in some countries where there is sufficient daily sun for heating domestic hot water. The equipment is usually inexpensive and simple to instal and operate. A very simple pillow-type collector is widely used in Japan (see fig. 11). The collector is simply placed on the roof of the house and filled with water in the morning. The sun heats the water all day so that when the family returns in the evening there is sufficient hot water for bathing. In countries such as Japan and Israel where fuels are expensive, the cost of a simple collector is soon recovered.

Already in Britain and in the USA the cost of fuel has made solar energy an economic means of heating swimming pools. As the temperature of the heated water is lower than is generally required for space heating, the collector can be simpler in design, with maybe a covering of one sheet of glass, and hence cheaper to build and to purchase. Solar collectors for swimming-pool heating are marketed both in Britain and in the USA. The collectors are usually installed in south-facing rows alongside the pool or on a nearby roof if suitable. For installations for space heating, however, it will probably be necessary to construct purpose-built collectors. Collectors for space heating have not yet been manufactured because a high capital investment would be required in order to market a product which has not yet been shown to be economically possible.

Despite the economic unattractiveness of the use of solar energy for space heating at present, it is possible to extrapolate present trends in the demand for and cost of energy to arrive at one firm conclusion: the cost of fuels must continue to rise. The more detailed estimation of by how much or how soon this will happen is, however, open to a much wider interpretation. Accepting the first conclusion, solar energy has already been acclaimed as an income-energy source which could form a large part of our future fuel budget. Plans for its exploitation range from solar farms, where banks of collectors are ranged over vast acres of land in sunny parts of the world with satellite power stations receiving all available energy above the atmosphere and beaming the energy back to earth as microwave power to a receiving station, to the other extreme of every house being equipped to collect all the energy falling upon it and utilize it within the building fabric. Although the latter system corresponds directly with the actual distribution of regular amounts of energy falling everywhere on the earth, the large-scale solution might well be the more likely to be developed in the future. Money is always more readily available for the establishment of large prestige projects which can be controlled easily by large industries or governments, than for the rehabilitation of old houses in order to insulate walls and roofs and draughtproof ill-fitting windows and doors, although this would

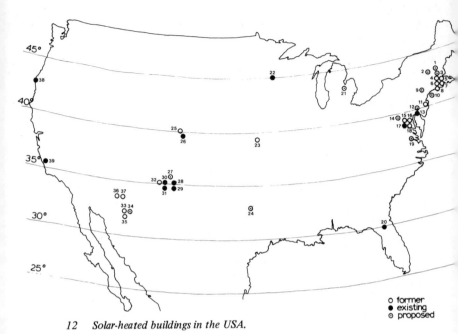

12   Solar-heated buildings in the USA.

o former
● existing
◎ proposed

1 GSA office building; Manchester, N.H.
2 Grassy Brook Village; Newfane, Vt.
3 Audubon Society; Lincoln, Mass.
4 MIT house 1; Cambridge, Mass.
5 MIT house 2; Cambridge, Mass.
6 MIT house 3; Cambridge, Mass.
7 MIT house 4; Cambridge, Mass.
8 Telkes-Raymond-Peabody house; Dover, Mass.
9 Cary Arboretum; Millbrook, N.Y.
10 Grumman Aerospace; Bethpage, N.Y.
11 Laboratory; Princeton, N.J.
12 Academy of Natural Sciences; Philadelphia, Pa.
13 University of Delaware Solar One; Newark, Del.
14 Wilson house; Martinsburg, Va.
15 Thomason house 1; Washington, D.C.
16 Thomason house 2; Washington, D.C.
17 Thomason house 3; Washington, D.C.
18 Thomason house 4; Washington, D.C.
19 NASA Langley Center; Langley, Va.

20 University of Florida solar house; Gainesville, Fla.
21 GSA Post Office; Saginaw, Mich.
22 Project Ouroboros; Minneapolis, Minn.
23 Earl Palmberg residence; Topeka, Kan.
24 Blum apartment complex; Dallas, Tex.
25 Löf house; Boulder, Colo.
26 Löf house; Denver, Colo.
27 Sun Mountain; Santa Fe, N.M.
28, 29 Integrated Life-Support Systems Lab; Tijeras, N.M.
30, 31 Baer house; Albuquerque, N.M.
32 Solar office building; Albuquerque, N.M.
33 University of Arizona lab; Tucson, Ariz.
34 Meinel house; Tucson, Ariz.
35 US Forest Service Desert Grassland Station; Amado, Ariz.
36 Hay-Yellott test building; Phoenix, Ariz.
37 AFASE competition house; Phoenix, Ariz.
38 Solar house; Coos Bay, Ore.
39 Hay house; Atascadero, Cal.

probably provide a much more immediate saving in total fuel expenditure. As twenty to thirty per cent of the total energy consumption of both Britain and the USA is spent on home heating, a worthwhile decrease in the total fuel consumed could easily be achieved with some capital investment in income-energy equipment. It may be that as energy becomes scarcer and running costs more expensive, capital expenditure on small-scale systems may become more attractive, although the search for dramatic replacements for traditional power stations and energy grids, whether nuclear or solar, and the comforting extension of the status quo, will probably seem the more attractive point for the investment of money by those who have it.

Most of the solar-heated houses that have been constructed to date are in the USA (see fig. 12), although some experiments have been carried out in Europe. The early houses built in 1950 or before often appear very traditional in design, with the solar power system plumbed into the structure. The Boulder house (Löf, 1956) demonstrates this approach, as the house was converted to partial heating by solar energy without any great modification to the existing hot-air system, the only structural modifications being the cutting of slots in the upper and lower edges of the roof to allow the air to flow through the collector panels, and the construction of some additional air ducts. A gravel-filled heat storage bed was excavated in the basement of the house but without affecting the existing structure. The system is shown in fig. 13. Once the collector has been raised to a high enough temperature by the sun for collection of energy to become economic, the cold return air from the rooms is blown through the collector. As long as the sun shines, the air is circulated through the collector to the rooms. When the quantity of energy collected is greater than that needed for house heating, some of the air is diverted through the gravel storage bed where the heat it contains is transferred to the gravel. On days when there is insufficient or no sun, air can be blown from the house through the gravel bed where it picks up the stored heat before being fed back to the rooms. When the temperature of the air coming from the storage bed is too low, auxiliary heat is supplied to the air from the gas boiler. In this way the total amount of fuel consumed by the boiler is decreased, as the air is preheated by the stored solar energy. In summer, when the heating system is no longer required, the hot air from the collector is diverted through a heat exchanger before being exhausted to the outside. In the heat exchanger the heat from the air is transferred to water circulating from a 364-litre hot-water tank, which in turn supplies the hot water to the house for baths, washing up, etc.

During its first winter of operation the solar heating system in the Boulder house supplied 25.6 per cent of the total heat required for

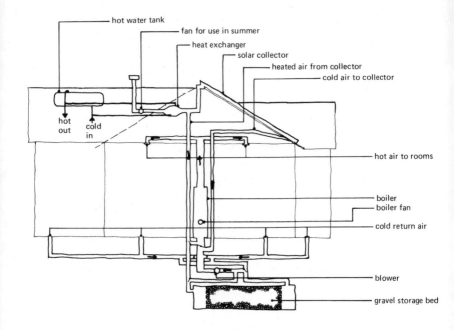

13 The Boulder house (after Löf, 1956). The solar heating system of the Boulder house and (below) a view of the south side.

space heating from September to May inclusive. This figure would have been larger but for the fact that some of the glass which had not been given sufficient tolerances had broken under thermal stresses at the beginning and this was not replaced until after the first winter. Moreover, the solar heating system was completely or partially out of operation for six weeks. Although this system provided part of the heating load, 49 per cent more electricity had to be supplied to power the additional

34

fan and blower. Nevertheless, a 15.7 per cent cost saving on the total winter fuel bill was achieved. No records of the cost of installing the additional solar heating system are available, but from the small saving in fuel over the first winter of operation the system was probably not economic.

A water-based solar heating system operates in much the same way as the air system of the Boulder house. Such a system was built and operated in the Massachusetts Institute of Technology (MIT) solar house IV (see fig. 14). which was designed to obtain 75 per cent of its heating requirements from the sun. The flat-plate collector actually formed the roof of the purpose-built house, unlike the case of the Boulder house where the collector panels had to be fitted awkwardly around an existing gable. The collector was made of a metal plate with tubes fixed on to the back through which the water was pumped. Having been heated, the water was pumped to a hot-water storage tank which was sized to provide sufficient stored heat for one heating degree day (defined as the summation of the temperature differences between the heated interior temperature and the average outdoor temperature for each day in the heating season, divided by the number of days). The auxiliary heating system was therefore sized to meet the maximum heating demand for periods of overcast weather. The expansion tank relieved fluctuations in pressure with the changing water temperature and also allowed for the collector to be drained of water when not in use, to prevent freezing. As long as the temperature of the storage tank was 28° C or higher, the hot water was pumped through a heat exchanger over which air was blown. The heated air was then distributed to the rooms. If the water temperature of the tank dropped below 28° C it became, in energy terms, no longer economic to operate all the pumps and fans to reclaim this low-temperature heat, and then the oil-fired boiler was used. This auxiliary boiler also heated the domestic hot water.

For two consecutive winters the solar heating system provided 48 per cent and 57 per cent of the total heat requirement. Again, the cost of providing, in effect, two heating systems is high, even though the use of the collector as the roof covering produced some saving. In the MIT house air had to be used as the heat distribution medium, even though water was used elsewhere in the system, as the temperature of the solar-heated water (40° − 46° C) is too low for use in a normal radiator system. Apart from radiant ceiling or wall panels using low-temperature water, air is the only method of distributing low-temperature heat satisfactorily, even though air heating does not produce the more comfortable conditions of a radiant source of heat, whether high-temperature water, electric fire or coal fire.

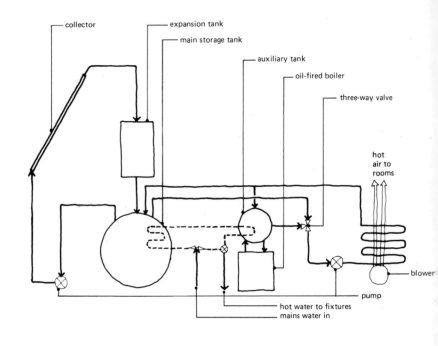

- collector
- expansion tank
- main storage tank
- auxiliary tank
- oil-fired boiler
- three-way valve

hot
air to
rooms

- blower
- pump
- hot water to fixtures
- mains water in

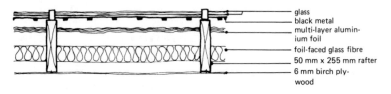

- glass
- black metal
- multi-layer alumin-
  ium foil
- foil-faced glass fibre
- 50 mm x 255 mm rafter
- 6 mm birch ply-
  wood

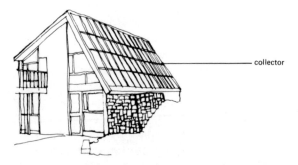

- collector

14   The MIT solar house IV (after Engebretson, 1961). The solar heating system, with (centre) a section through the collector and (below) an outside view showing the collector installation.

36

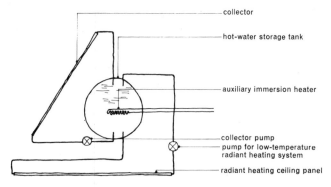

- collector
- hot-water storage tank
- auxiliary immersion heater
- collector pump
- pump for low-temperature radiant heating system
- radiant heating ceiling panel

15   The MIT solar house III: solar heating system (after Anderson, 1973). The solar house system shown above was adapted from an original laboratory test system, where the building was divided into compartments to test different storage systems. The collector was positioned on the gable, which in turn sat on the roof of the single-storey living area. The gable also housed a hot-water storage tank with a capacity of 5,455 litres, which was designed to give two days' storage. The house was heated by low-temperature radiant ceiling panels, with a back-up system of three 4 kW immersion heaters in the storage tank. The collector operated at 30 per cent efficiency. South-facing windows at ground-floor level increased the direct solar gain to the house but, of the remainder of the heat required, the solar heating system provided approximately 50 per cent in January and February and 80 per cent or more for the remainder of the October-April period. This was increased, when modifications evened out the water flow over the collector surface, to 63 per cent in January and 75 per cent or more the rest of the time.

Other solar house heating systems which have been built and tested are shown in figs. 15 – 33, most following after the pattern of the two houses described above. Differences arise in the form of the collector and the type and size of the storage medium. The use in the Dover house (fig. 22) of a chemical method of storing heat is important, but this will be discussed in more detail in Chapter 8, 'Storing heat'. In every design some evaluation of the cost of the solar heating system and storage must be made and compared with the cost of supplying auxiliary heating from conventional sources. The costs are assessed in terms of the materials used, the amount of useful floor space taken up by the system and especially by the storage, and the additional energy, if any, that must be put in to operate the system. Thus, in order to make the solar heating system as economic as possible, most systems provide partial solar heating with only one or two days' storage. However, in the autonomous context, even though capital costs are important, assuming that conventional fuels are at a premium the balance may be shifted towards less auxiliary heating and a greater storage capacity. This will in turn depend upon the level of comfort required by the occupants as,

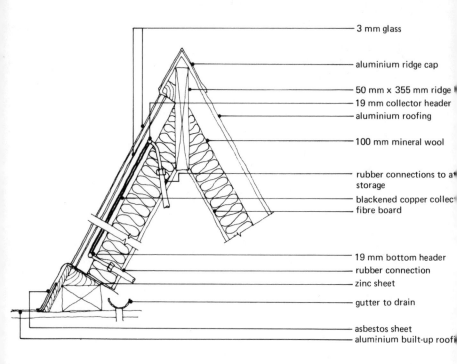

- 3 mm glass
- aluminium ridge cap
- 50 mm x 355 mm ridge
- 19 mm collector header
- aluminium roofing
- 100 mm mineral wool
- rubber connections to storage
- blackened copper collector
- fibre board
- 19 mm bottom header
- rubber connection
- zinc sheet
- gutter to drain
- asbestos sheet
- aluminium built-up roof

16   MIT solar house III (after Proceedings of Conference on Applied Solar Energy, *1956). The details of the collector, with (below) an outside view showing the installation.*

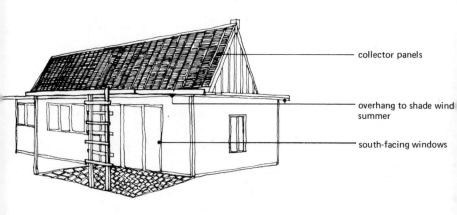

- collector panels
- overhang to shade window summer
- south-facing windows

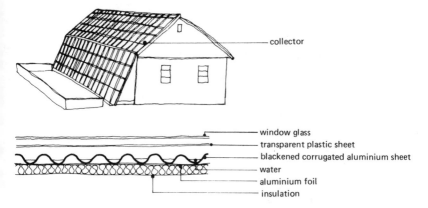

window glass
transparent plastic sheet
blackened corrugated aluminium sheet
water
aluminium foil
insulation

17   Thomason solar-heated house No. 1 (after Thomason, 1961). In the Thomason collector (above), water is pumped up to a manifold distributor mounted at the head of the blackened corrugated aluminium sheets. It then flows down the corrugations, is heated as it passes over the hot metal and collected at the base of the collector before passing to the heat storage bin. The collector is covered with a layer of glass and one of clear plastic and is cheaper to construct than the conventional tube-in-strip type, although a pump is necessary for the operation of the system. The outside view (top) shows the collector installation.

if auxiliary heating was seen in terms of additional layers of clothing, the solar heating system, with as large a storage volume as could be practically supplied with the money available, could be used.

The houses described also show the problem of using a low-temperature method of house heating. Air is the most satisfactory method of distributing heat at 30° C or upwards although it does not provide the most comfortable conditions. A person feels uncomfortable when his body is radiating heat outwards to surrounding cold surfaces even though the actual air temperature is high. When the body is receiving radiant heat from a fire, a radiator or the sun, however, a lower air temperature can be tolerated while the person feels comfortably warm. It is this fact that makes it possible for people to sunbathe high up in the Alps where the air is clear, so that a great deal of solar radiation reaches the ground, but cold. This means that most solar heating systems, while nearly always costing more than a conventional heating system, even allowing for the fact that the energy for running the system is free, also produce inferior comfort conditions within the building. However, if conventional fuels do increase in price or are even rationed in supply, then solar heating systems will become competitive to instal. Even if the building cannot be heated continuously through the winter, as the storage may be insufficient for long overcast periods, at least some air-distributed solar heat may be better than no heat at all.

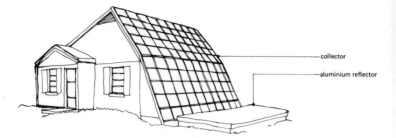

collector

aluminium reflector

18a   *Thomason solar-heated house No. 2 (after Thomason, 1961). This has been designed with an additional aluminium reflector extending out at the base of the collector. It reflects heat on to the collector to increase the total heat output by 15–30 per cent.*

collector

reflector on roof
of sun porch

18b   *In Thomason house no. 3, the collector is positioned on the steep side of the roof only, and the aluminium reflector is formed by the slightly sloping roof of the sunporch in order to be invisible from the ground. This also prevents collector and reflector from being shaded by trees.*

collector of asphalt shingles

insulation

water

polythene liner and cover
to pond under floor

18c   *House no. 4 was designed as a low-cost cottage or second home. The asphalt shingle collector was not as efficient as the aluminium one, and was also prone to leaks. Difficulty was experienced with the polythene liner, as it was impossible to obtain one completely free of pin-holes. The system operated by heating water in the collector and storing the hot water in the pond under the house.*

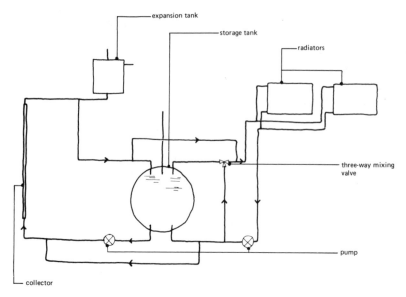

*19   Swedish solar-heated house at Capri (after Pleijel and Lindström, 1961).
The collectors are placed vertically on the south-west-facing wall of the building,
which houses both a laboratory and living quarters. The orientation means an
estimated reduction of 20 per cent of the maximum possible radiation received.
A normal radiator system is operated at a temperature of 40° C, which means
that the radiators are just warm to the touch. A stove has been installed in the
living quarters and portable electric radiators in the laboratories for auxiliary
heating. Water is supplied to the radiators, mixed with the return water at 35° C,
either direct from the collector or from the 3,000-litre storage tank, depending
on the weather conditions. The radiators used for the collector were ordinary
Swedish central-heating radiators painted black on one side. The system was
designed to provide only partial solar heating.*

Since the design and construction of most of the solar houses
described, improvements have been made in insulation materials, so
that the over-all heating demands of a house can now be reduced. If the
amount of air infiltrating into the house can also be reduced to the
minimum required by law, then the heat lost through ventilating cold
air into the house can be reduced in proportion. The actual heat put
into the building to maintain an adequate indoor temperature is then
reduced, and even the direct solar gain through windows becomes a
large part of this required heat. This fact has been exploited in a
number of more recent solar-heated buildings where collectors have
been constructed which are simple developments of the window. The
solar energy is now collected, stored and then re-radiated to the inside

41

of the house without any of the array of bits and pieces necessary in a 'conventional' solar heating system.

The best-known building of this type in England, St George's School near Wallasey, Cheshire, has, in fact, no more than a very large double-glazed window across the south side of the building. The remainder of the structure is made of mass materials, heavily insulated, and the building is well sealed to reduce the number of air changes per hour to one or less. This value is actually too low for a school but represents the probable limit for a house. The building is long and thin to obtain a maximum area of south-facing glass wall. The structure, apart from the glass wall, is made of brickwork with the roof and floors of heavy reinforced concrete, all insulated on the outside face with 127 mm of expanded polystyrene. The south wall is made of two diffusing glass leaves spaced 610 mm apart, although 8 per cent of the area of the wall is formed of well-sealed single-glazed windows which can be opened

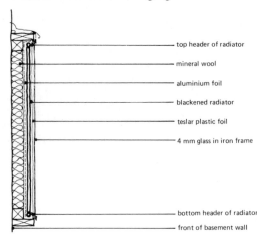

- top header of radiator
- mineral wool
- aluminium foil
- blackened radiator
- teslar plastic foil
- 4 mm glass in iron frame
- bottom header of radiator
- front of basement wall

20 South-west elevation of Swedish solar house at Capri (after Pleijel and Lindström, 1961). (Left) Vertical section through the collector.

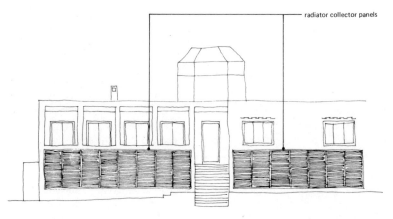

- radiator collector panels

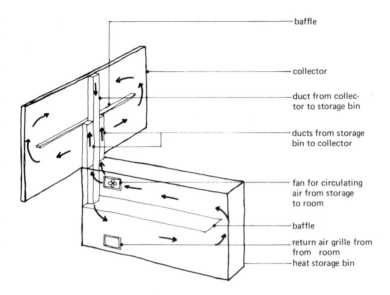

baffle

collector

duct from collector to storage bin

ducts from storage bin to collector

fan for circulating air from storage to room

baffle

return air grille from from room

heat storage bin

21 The Telkes-Raymond-Peabody solar-heated house at Dover, Massachusetts (after Zarem, 1963). The diagram shows the collector panel linked to a storage bin of hydrated sodium sulphate (Glauber's salts). The house contained three such bins, each linked to a third of the collector, which ran the full length of the south façade. Air was blown through the collector panel and down into the storage bin, where the heated air melted the salts. The cooled air then returned to the collector. Heat could be supplied to each individual room as required. A small fan in each room blew air from the storage, the salts giving out heat as they solidified. The bins were formed of stacks of 23-litre cans containing the salts. Although the heat gained from the collector and through the ground-floor windows was sufficient at first, auxiliary heating was later put in to meet more severe winter conditions and to compensate for the fact that over a number of heating/cooling cycles the salts tend to separate into their two phases and the storage capacity is thus reduced.

for ventilation. Heat is therefore supplied to the building from the sun, from the occupants and from the tungsten light fittings, the temperature of the room being controlled by opening the windows. Although former studies (*Architect's Journal*, 1969) have doubted the validity of the method of heating the school by solar energy, especially as the low ventilation rate made the building smelly, and the large areas of glass at times produced glare conditions within the classrooms, a more recent study (Davies, 1971) found that when the sun was shining the solar radiation formed the principal source of heat in the building. On a sunny winter day the solar energy input reached a value of nearly 90 watts per square metre (this represents the daily total averaged over the 24-hour period, referred to a unit area of the solid wall).

This compares with an equivalent value of 11 W/m^2 for body heat and 25 W/m^2 as the heat gained from the tungsten light fittings in winter. On a cloudy day in winter, the value for the solar radiation was found to fall to about 12 W/m^2 (occupants 14 W/m^2 and lighting 38 W/m^2). However, the high thermal capacity of the building structure, combined with the low ventilation rate, means that the surfaces of the building remain at a constant temperature, and changes in the external conditions take as much as a week before they are registered inside the building. The internal temperature of the building can thus be maintained without any external power sources apart from the electricity in the lights, and although a back-up system was originally installed by the local authority, it was later removed after it was found to be unnecessary in the extremely cold winter of 1962-3. Such a system could probably be applied more acceptably to a house, where intermittent heating is not a problem as the house is generally occupied throughout the day, and where lower ventilation rates are more tolerable.

The idea of designing a passive collector, such as the south-facing wall at Wallasey, where air or water does not have to be driven over the collecting surface, has been taken up and sophisticated in further

22   The Dover solar-heated house (after Zarem, 1963). (Below) Detail of the solar collector.

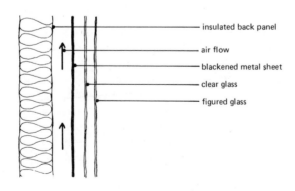

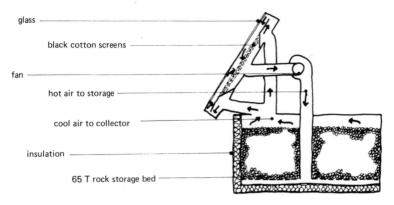

glass
black cotton screens
fan
hot air to storage
cool air to collector
insulation
65 T rock storage bed

*23   The Donovan and Bliss house (after Anderson, 1973). This was a system
for 100 per cent solar space heating designed in 1954 for an existing light-framed
structure 48 kilometres south of Tucson, Arizona. The collector and storage
system shown above were constructed separately from the house. The collector
was made of four black cotton screens 6 mm apart covered with a glass sheet
and tilted so as to be perpendicular to the sun in January. Air was warmed as it
was blown across the screen, the heat being stored in an insulated bed of rock
of 100 mm average diameter. On a clear day the 30 m² collector collected twice
as much energy as the average daily requirement for heating the house. For
summer cooling the air was blown over a separate horizontal screen before being
passed through the storage bed to lower the temperature of the rocks, thus
providing a cold sink for cooling the house the next day. There is no record of
how the cotton screens performed over a period of time, but with the high
temperatures involved they would probably deteriorate faster than a conventional flat-plate collector.*

designs and experiments in France and America. F. Trombe and J.
Michel developed a system in France for using the south-facing walls of
the house, rather than windows, as vertical solar collectors. The south-
facing wall is made of concrete, painted black on the outside and
covered with a double sheet of glass. It acts as both absorber and heat
store. Slots are incorporated at the top and base of the wall (see fig. 27).
As the air is heated by the black wall it rises by natural convection and
passes through the slots into the room, to be replaced by colder air
flowing in at the base of the wall. In this way a thermosiphoning
system is established, with the warm air feeding directly into the space
to be heated. On a sunny day the wall will have absorbed sufficient
heat to continue the thermosiphoning action through the evening and
night, but a longer period of storage is not possible with this type of
collector. The prototype houses built at Montlouis in the Pyrenees with
this type of passive collector forming the south-facing wall derived two-
thirds to three-quarters of the heating load from the solar wall. The

45

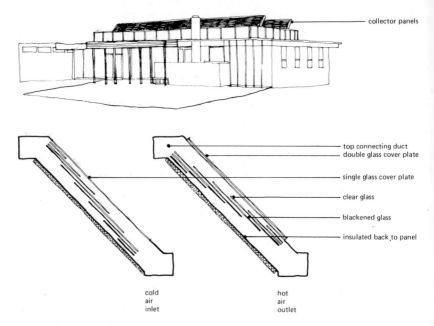

collector panels

top connecting duct
double glass cover plate

single glass cover plate

clear glass

blackened glass

insulated back to panel

cold
air
inlet

hot
air
outlet

*24 (Top)   The Löf solar-heated house at Denver, Colorado (after Löf, 1961).
(Above) Details of the collector. The cold air is first heated in a 'low-temperature'
collector, with only a single glass cover sheet, before passing through the 'high-
temperature' collector which is double-glazed.*

houses are one room thick, each room having a solar wall, while the
remainder of the house is constructed as a light, well-insulated frame
building with a U-value of 0.5 W/m^2 deg C. (The U-value of a wall is the
measure of its ability to transmit heat, and hence depends on the
thickness and the material of which the wall is made. In Britain a
minimum U-value of 1.0 W/m^2 deg C is statutory, which is equivalent to
a 280-mm cavity brick wall with inner leaf of insulating blockwork.)

However, in the Pyrenees where the air is clear but cold, the amount
of radiation received on the vertical surface of the wall on a sunny day
is very high, 6 to 7 kilowatt-hours per square metre per day. When a
similar system is applied to the British climate, where over-all insolation
levels are lower even if the ambient winter temperature is higher, the
energy received drops to less than 2 kWh/m^2/day during periods of
bright sunshine. This gives an estimated input to the house of about
1 kWh/m^2/day, provided that the day has six continuous hours of
sunshine. If the heat received by the wall were used to heat the room

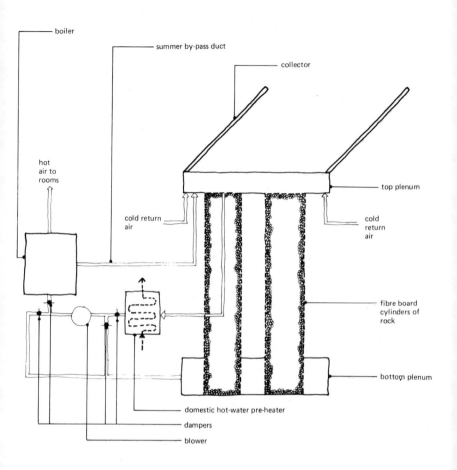

boiler

summer by-pass duct

collector

hot
air to
rooms

top plenum

cold return
air

cold
return
air

fibre board
cylinders of
rock

bottom plenum

domestic hot-water pre-heater

dampers

blower

25   The Löf house, Denver: air and water heating system (after Löf, 1961).
*Air is warmed in the collector made of overlapping sheets of glass and is stored
in the fibreboard cylinders of 25-40 mm rock situated within the house. By
operating the various dampers shown above, the house can be heated directly
from the collector, or from storage, or the heat from the solar collector can be
stored in the rock. The natural-gas boiler can be used as part of the first two
cycles to supplement the heat supplied to the house. Hot air from the
collector flows through the water pre-heater before returning to the collector
to provide some heating of the domestic hot water. In summer, the collector
can be operated so that the air only flows through the pre-heater and then
back to the collector via the by-pass duct. During the heating season the
collector efficiency was 35 per cent, and the solar heating system provided 25
per cent of the heating load. Of the useful heat collected, only 7 per cent
was used for water pre-heating, the remaining 93 per cent being used for
space heating. The Löf collector at Denver has been providing 25 per cent of
the winter heating load for the past fifteen years, the auxiliary heat being supplied by the natural-gas boiler. Air losses through leakage between the various
parts of the equipment are always a problem in any solar air system.*

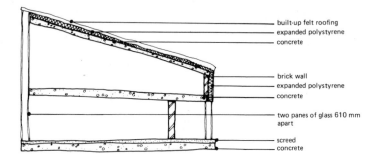

built-up felt roofing
expanded polystyrene
concrete

brick wall
expanded polystyrene
concrete

two panes of glass 610 mm apart

screed
concrete

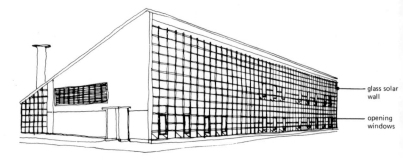

glass solar wall

opening windows

26   *St George's School, Wallasey (after Moorcraft, 1973).*

during periods without sunshine, insulated shutters would have to be provided. These could be closed over the glass on the outside of the wall and would reduce the loss of the collected heat. Without such shutters the solar wall would only be effective when the sun was shining. Compared with the heating load provided in the Pyrenean prototype, this type of passive solar collector would, in Britain, contribute only marginally to the total space-heating load. Nevertheless, it is a cheap form of collector with no running costs as no moving parts are involved.

In two schemes in America, water rather than concrete has formed the short-term storage for two passive collector designs. Harold Hay has developed a system of water-filled ponds supported by the roof of the house and covered with movable insulated shutters. Hay has designed two buildings heated in this way: a test room in Phoenix, Arizona, and the later, more sophisticated Solarchitecture House in California. In the small test room transparent plastic bags were filled with water to a depth of 150–180 mm and these were supported on a metal decking with a black plastic lining sheet between the two. The horizontal movable insulated shutters were supported above the ponds

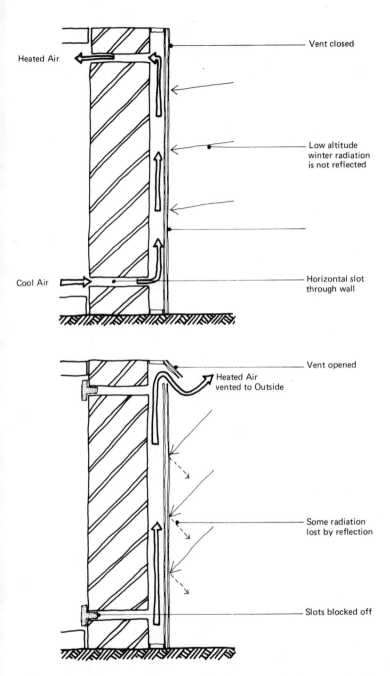

Vent closed

Heated Air

Low altitude
winter radiation
is not reflected

Cool Air

Horizontal slot
through wall

Vent opened

Heated Air
vented to Outside

Some radiation
lost by reflection

Slots blocked off

27 *Passive solar collector: different modes of operation for winter (top) and summer.*

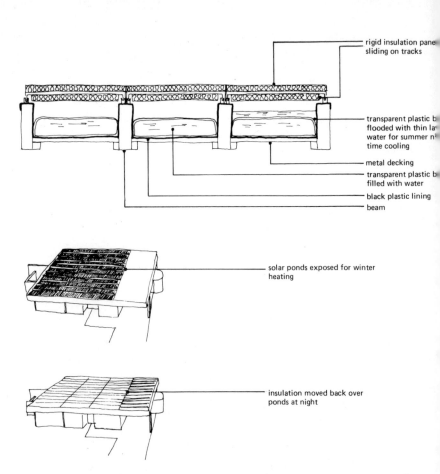

rigid insulation panel sliding on tracks

transparent plastic bag flooded with thin layer water for summer night-time cooling

metal decking

transparent plastic bag filled with water

black plastic lining

beam

solar ponds exposed for winter heating

insulation moved back over ponds at night

28   Solarchitecture house by Harold Hay. When the solar ponds are exposed
for winter heating, the sliding insulation panels can be stacked over the carport
or patio, to be slid back over the ponds at night.

on aluminium tracks. The black lining absorbed the incoming solar
radiation during the day and the water in the plastic bags was heated.
An hour before sunset the horizontal shutters were slid back to cover
the ponds and the building was heated all night by the absorbed heat
radiating from the ceiling into the room. The shutters were opened
again an hour after sunrise. The cycle is reversible so that the house
can be cooled during the day by exposing the ponds to the clear night
skies in summer. This type of system is best suited to the desert climate
of south-west America, where there is adequate solar radiation to heat
the ponds during the day despite a lower outdoor temperature. In this
type of climate a system that provides both winter heating and summer
cooling is an additional cost benefit.

The Solarchitecture house in California is being built at a higher latitude and although summer cooling can easily be achieved, it is more difficult to collect sufficient solar energy for winter heating. An extra sheet of clear plastic supported by the aluminium tracks is necessary to increase the efficiency of the roof collector and hence the amount of solar energy that can be used for space heating. In the California house the heat from the roof ponds is supplemented by a patented south-facing wall construction of hollow concrete blocks with tubular plastic liners placed in the cavities which are filled with water. Movable vertical insulated shutters are used to restrict the heat loss from this wall at night in winter and, as in the Phoenix house, movable horizontal shutters are used to cover the roof ponds. The shutters are operated by simply pulling a rope and, although the system has no other mechanical parts and is simple to operate, the complexity of the tracks and their supports increases the initial cost of the simplified solar heating system.

Much the same principle has been used by Steve Baer at his home in Albuquerque, although here the components of the system have been chosen to be as cheap and as simple to build and operate as possible. The house, or 'zome', is a dome whose generating principles have been adjusted so that the components are easier to standardize. The south-facing wall of the zome is made up of a wooden rack supporting 55-gallon oil drums lying horizontally. These are painted black and filled with water. The drums and their framework are covered with a double sheet of glass to reduce the heat loss from them, and an insulated shutter hinged to the bottom of the wall can easily be raised and lowered to conserve heat at night and during overcast weather. In the lowered position the insulated doors, which are faced with aluminium, reflect a portion of the radiation falling on them on to the collector and hence augment the total solar energy available. In operation the

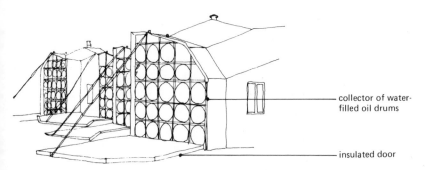

collector of water-filled oil drums

insulated door

29 Steve Baer's solar-heated zome.

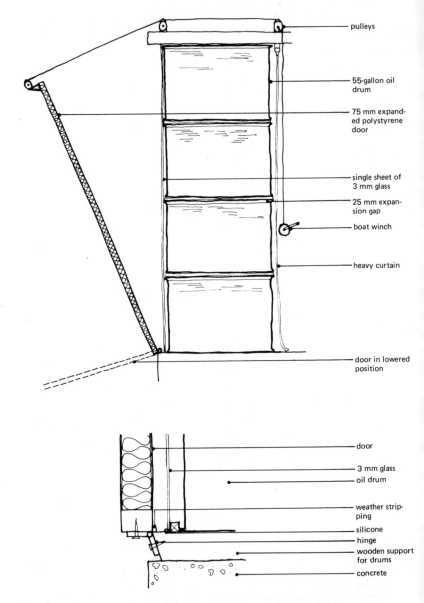

— pulleys

— 55-gallon oil drum

— 75 mm expanded polystyrene door

— single sheet of 3 mm glass

— 25 mm expansion gap

— boat winch

— heavy curtain

— door in lowered position

— door

— 3 mm glass
— oil drum

— weather stripping

— silicone
— hinge
— wooden support for drums
— concrete

30   Details of collector for Zomeworks (after Baer, 1973). The expanded polystyrene door, which slopes in the lowered position to allow rain to run off, is faced with aluminium to reflect sunlight on to the collector when it is lowered. The curtain on the interior side helps to regulate the flow of the heat stored in the drums.

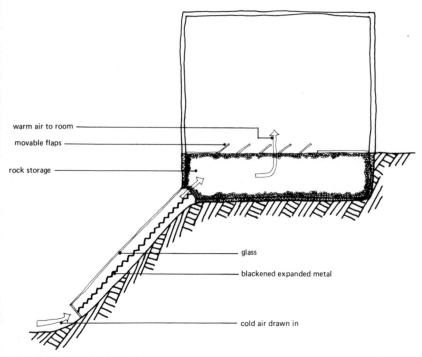

warm air to room

movable flaps

rock storage

glass

blackened expanded metal

cold air drawn in

31   Solar house by Steve Baer.

wall collected $3.8 - 4.1$ kWh/m^2 on a clear day. Baer (1973) suggests using a heavy curtain on the inside of the wall to help regulate the flow of heat from the warmed water in the drums into the house. The zome is simply heated by the radiation into the room from the solar wall. Again, such a system is probably best suited to a desert climate where solar incidence is high in the winter and where storage for a period of overcast weather is not such a problem.

Another house near by, also constructed by Baer, which is reported to work better in practice than the Zomeworks solar heater, is shown in fig. 31. Here a more conventional house is constructed on a slope over a heat storage bed of gravel. The expanded metal in the collector heats up and air is drawn up over it by natural convection to warm the gravel bed. Adjustable vents in the floor allow the warm air to pass from the gravel bed into the room.

All the systems demonstrate the problem of trying to transport solar energy from its point of collection outside the building to the interior where the heat is required. Only Wallasey school, greenhouses and similar sun-tempered insulated buildings where the heat loss is low or unimportant can use the energy that actually falls within the

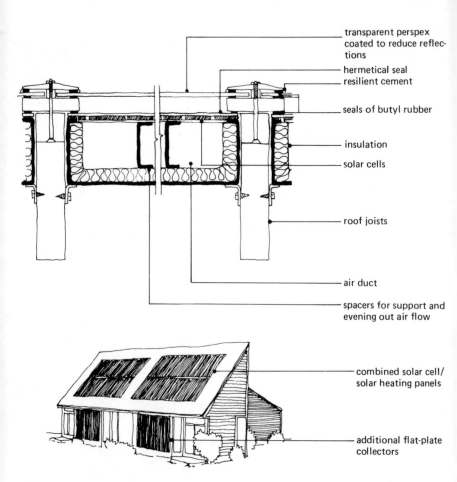

transparent perspex coated to reduce reflections

hermetical seal resilient cement

seals of butyl rubber

insulation

solar cells

roof joists

air duct

spacers for support and evening out air flow

combined solar cell/ solar heating panels

additional flat-plate collectors

32   Solar One, built at the University of Delaware (after Boer, 1973). (Top) Detail of the combined solar cell/solar heating panels.

building. Otherwise heat must be collected and used in a conventional air-heating system where the lower temperatures are satisfactory; or, if higher collection temperatures can be achieved, heated water can be used in low-temperature radiant ceiling and wall panels. Alternatively, in areas where winter insolation is relatively high and frequent, large areas of the passive type of solar collector can be heated up and used as a large low-temperature source of radiant heat within the building. In order to maintain the present standards of comfort in heating which the growing use of central-heating systems has fostered, higher temperatures must be used in collecting solar energy. This suggests the use of focusing collectors.

54

A focusing collector, which is usually parabolic in shape, operates by concentrating the sun's rays on to a single point at the focus of the collector where a high temperature can therefore be achieved. Focusing collectors have been built and operated in sizes ranging from the solar furnace built into a hillside in the Pyrenees, which is capable of producing temperatures of $3,000^\circ$ C, to small cookers for developing countries. No one, however, seems to have built and operated a focusing collector for heating water to or near boiling-point for direct use for domestic space heating and hot-water supply, even though it is theoretically possible to mount such a collector on the roof of a house in the same way as a flat-plate installation. Focusing collectors are more difficult and expensive to construct and require more complicated mounting, although Moorcraft (1973) suggests that the added complexities of constant tracking and adjustment probably do not apply to the domestic situation. However, no one has yet thought it worth while, despite the many experiments in collector design and solar heating systems, to build and test an integrated focusing collector system. In effect, simple long parabolic collectors mounted in the east—west position on the roof might need adjusting only weekly or monthly, and black tubes of water passing along the focus of the collector could be heated to high temperatures during periods of direct radiation. Daniels (1964) describes a solar cooker, 1.2 m in diameter, with an area of about 1.1 m^2, focusing on to a kettle with an area of 0.03 m^2 which produced a temperature of approximately 150° C. However, the higher temperatures mean that the heat lost from the collector also increases and the over-all efficiency of collection drops. Also, unlike the lower-temperature flat-plate collectors, where a portion of the total energy collected is made up of indirect radiation, the focusing collector will focus only direct sunlight. This dependence upon direct sunlight in a temperate climate argues against focusing collectors, as does the ability to heat water only to relatively low temperatures against flat-plate collectors. Both systems, therefore, have advantages and disadvantages and might usefully be combined. Water heated to a low temperature in a flat-plate collector might be pumped automatically through a focusing collector during periods of bright sunshine to boost its temperature. However, the increasing complexity and multiplicity of equipment will always raise the cost of the system, probably beyond the returns that can be expected from it.

Only one other method of using solar energy for space heating remains a possibility. Research into space flights of long duration has accelerated the development of increased efficiency and lower cost for solar cells. Nevertheless, the amount of electricity generated by the direct conversion of solar energy to electricity would be probably

55

insufficient and certainly uneconomic if used as a source of direct radiant heat for houses. Of the four methods of converting solar energy into electricity, photovoltaic cells have proved the most efficient in use as well as being simple to fabricate and long-lived provided certain favourable conditions are maintained. However, the price of such cells makes the production of electricity in this way very expensive. In 1961, silicon crystal cells were quoted at a price of $175 per watt. New developments have led to the creation of thin polycrystalline film cadmium sulphide cells which have greater efficiencies of conversion, over 8 per cent in direct sunlight, and which could be marketed for as little as $1 per watt if mass-produced. Nevertheless, at 5 per cent : conversion efficiency, 20 m^2 of solar cells would be necessary to produce 1 kW of power at a best possible and hitherto unrealized cost of $1000. Since direct conversion is expensive, even in the future its application will probably be limited to essential electrical supplies such as lighting and telecommunications. These uses of electricity, if the lighting is limited to fluorescent tubes, have a high efficiency of conversion of electricity and hence increase the over-all efficiency of the solar-cell system. It is possible to increase the total power generated by focusing the solar energy on to the cells, but the cells must then be cooled, as the higher temperatures produced lower their efficiency of conversion.

The Delaware Solar One house uses this latter principle to form combined solar-cell/solar-air heating collectors (see fig. 33). An area of 71 m^2 is covered with solar cells on a roof sloping at 45° to the horizontal. The cells are linked to an 18-kWh lead-acid battery. Cadmium sulphide thin-film cells are used and their actual life will be discovered by the project, as most of these cells have, up till now, degraded when exposed to humid atmospheres at high temperatures. For this reason the operating efficiency of the cells will probably be below 7 per cent. Air is blown along the back of the cells, where it is warmed to 24° C before passing to a chemical storage bed. The cost of the solar cells for the Delaware house is not given; they are being fitted at the speed at which they can be made in the laboratory. When finished, the house is designed to obtain 80 per cent of its power and space heating from solar energy, the remainder being supplied from the grid, mostly at off-peak periods. Backed by the local utility company, it is an exercise in economy of power rather than total autonomy.

From all the preceding experiments, it is difficult to foresee how solar-heated buildings will develop. Flat-plate collectors have changed with the increasing costs of materials from the early examples in Florida made of copper to cheaper aluminium and steel versions, although the over-all operating efficiency of collection seems to depend

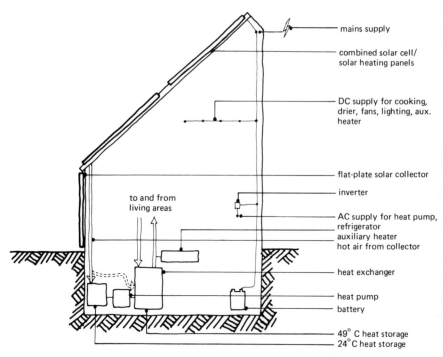

mains supply

combined solar cell/
solar heating panels

DC supply for cooking,
drier, fans, lighting, aux.
heater

flat-plate solar collector

inverter

AC supply for heat pump,
refrigerator
auxiliary heater
hot air from collector

heat exchanger

heat pump

battery

49° C heat storage
24° C heat storage

to and from
living areas

*33   Solar One, built at the University of Delaware (after Boer, 1973). Air is
heated to 24° C in the combined solar cell/solar heating panels on the roof in
early morning, and this heat is stored chemically in a eutectic mixture melting
near 24° C. At the same time, this heat is upgraded by the heat pump and
stored, again chemically, in a eutectic mixture melting at 49° C. Heat is extracted
from this source through a heat exchanger to heat the house. As the temperature
of the heated air rises during a sunny day, the heat pump is switched off and the
air passes directly to the 49° C storage. In the afternoon, as the temperature
drops, the heated air is again fed into the low-temperature storage. The house is
heated from the high-temperature storage in the early evening, the heat pump
being used to upgrade the low-temperature heat only during the later off-peak
electricity periods to charge up the high-temperature storage for the following
day. A day's storage of high-temperature heat is provided, auxiliary electric
heating being used during continuous cloudy days. The house is connected to the
mains grid at off-peak periods, that is during the night and early morning, and
at other times the solar-generated electricity is used to run appliances in the
house, the batteries supplying less than a full day's storage. The floor area of the
house is 140 m², and the area of the combined solar panels on the roof 71 m².
In addition six flat-plate collectors are placed on the south-facing wall to provide
supplementary heat during winter.*

very little on the materials used. Focusing collectors have not been tried in the domestic context and solar cells are still prohibitively expensive. The passive-type solar collectors work well in the climate and buildings designed for them. If conventional fuels are going to increase in cost and scarcity, then solar heating may once again be taken up and eulogized as a 'new' source of energy.

In the autonomous house the solar collector is the prime source of heat energy and, where the building is specially designed to meet these requirements, passive types of collector are cheap to build and simple to operate and could probably provide all the heating required in an insulated building. For the hot-water supply more conventional solar water-heating systems might be needed, although the Zomeworks system might be operated in a similar way to the Japanese pillow-type collector, where the hot water is drawn off at night and the collector refilled the next morning. In specially built structures the heating load can be alleviated by the amount of insulation incorporated, reduction of the ventilation heat loss, and design of the building to follow the climatic conditions. Houses would thus be designed, in the same way that Victorian greenhouses were designed, as optimum solutions for given energy conditions. Wallasey school illustrates this approach by the construction of a building of high thermal capacity with insulation on the outside surface to allow the walls to act as a heat store. In this way, the small quantities of incidental energy – that is the solar energy coming through the windows, body heat and waste heat from lighting – can be made to supply sufficient heat to maintain the temperature of the interior of the building, any fluctuations being supplemented by the heat stored in the mass of the structure.

When existing housing stock is under consideration, however, the solar heating system which follows conventional plumbing methods probably has more relevance to the problem than the design of the solar-tempered environment. Accepting that new buildings can be designed for adequate solar heating, a statement which still has to be borne out by experiment, there still remains the stock of poorly-insulated houses heated by conventional fuels. If solar energy is to be used for these buildings 'it will mean dollars to those who are the most clever in gadgeteering' (Glaser). If such a system of 'clip-on' solar heating components were to be developed, then the chance of optimizing the control of climate and income-energy sources for each individual house would be lost. Just as the microclimate varies, maybe infinitesimally, from one house to the next, so the individual systems should be designed with a similar precision.

For existing houses the first methods of conserving fuel would be by insulation and draught-sealing. Recently, a price of £600 was quoted

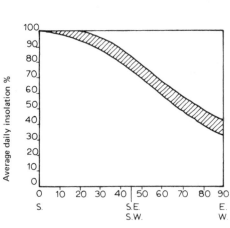

Average daily insolation %

Degree of deviation of wall from south

34   Range of variation of solar radiation falling on a vertical surface not facing due south (after Lorsch, 1972). The data are taken for various orientations of vertical collectors over most geographical locations in the USA (latitudes 30°-45°) for the critical winter months of December and January.

for the installation of gas central heating in a hundred-year-old terrace house which had been rehabilitated by the local authority in Cambridge as a demonstration home for four people. Assuming a terrace house of 5 m x 5 m x 5 m with 8 m^2 of window and door area, the capital cost involved in insulating this structure with 100 mm of expanded poly-styrene on the external walls and upper storey ceiling, and in placing new windows in the new external skin to reduce draughts, would be only £412 (insulation £98; rendering £124; battens £30; windows £160; prices taken from 'Current wage rates, market prices, and measured rates', *The Architect's Journal*, October 1973). Since the brickwork had to be repointed anyway, the costs would compare more favourably, as the new skin would provide effective waterproofing. With the money forming the difference between the two capital costs it should be possible to provide such a house with some form of solar water-heating system to provide at least hot water in summer. Much smaller amounts of conventional energy would then be needed to keep the house warm in winter than a full central-heating system would require. In nearly every case some portion of an existing house, whether roof or walls, can be found with a near-southerly aspect. Lorsch (1972) claims that a vertical collector facing south-east or south-west receives 80 per cent of the energy falling on a wall facing due south (see fig. 34). Such a collector could provide hot water or even some space heating. The

59

windows that receive sunlight would also contribute to the total heat gain to the house, as at Wallasey. Even if it was impossible to achieve full central heating, some fuel economy would be gained. The method at the end of the chapter summarizes the estimation of the performance of a typical flat-plate collector in Britain and gives some idea of the energy that might be collected.

If existing housing is to be converted to full or partial solar heating, then it will probably be better to sell the methods of conversion rather than completed pieces of equipment, in the same way that advice and grants are issued for the rehabilitation of hundred-year-old houses. A certain minimum standard of services is fixed, and the owner is at liberty to choose what extra services he wishes to instal with his own money. In the same way, the government could give grants for certain standards of insulation but the construction of solar collectors and full solar heating systems would be left to the owner, just as grants are given for a minimum heating system of a power point in every room while central heating is installed at the owner's cost. The owner would then have the option of investing more money in a system which would have zero or very low running costs, or paying for a decreased quantity of some fossil fuel, the cost of which is likely to rise in the future. Either way, the cost to society in terms of the total energy used in the domestic sector would be reduced. This principle could be further applied to water collection and purification and sewage disposal in an attempt to autonomize existing houses and relieve the increasing pressure on central plants. However, a full solar heating system is probably only possible in a purpose-built house. Even if the climate allows only low-temperature heating, maybe some heating, while not providing the ideal comfort conditions that the exploitation of fossil fuels has brought us to expect as a right, is better than no heating at all.

Estimation of the energy that could be collected by a solar collector to be built on an existing building

(The sunshine data used in this calculation are taken from the Kew records as these are the most detailed available. The variation between Kew and Cambridge, where the collector is to be built, is small.)

The roof to take the collector faces due south; the collector area = 15 m^2; the angle the collector makes with the horizontal = 23°.

To find the total energy that will be collected, both the direct solar energy and the indirect radiation must be considered. Although indirect radiation will be falling on the collector continuously, it can only be collected during periods of direct sunshine when the collector reaches a temperature high enough to make collection practical.

To calculate the monthly DIRECT energy receipt of a collector:

In a given month a collector at an angle θ to the horizontal receives
$$0.698 \, I \, n \sin(\theta + a) \text{ kWh/m}^2/\text{month}$$
where I is the average monthly intensity of direct solar radiation on days
of high radiation, measured in cal/cm^2/min on a surface normal
to the radiation
- n is the number of hours of bright sunshine in the month
- θ is the angle between the collector surface and the horizontal
- a is the average solar altitude in the month under consideration

To calculate the monthly INDIRECT energy receipt of a collector:

In a given month a collector at angle b to the horizontal receives
$$0.698 \, i \, n \, \tfrac{1}{2}(1 + \cos b) \text{ kWh/m}^2/\text{month}$$
of *collectable* indirect radiation,

where i is the average monthly background diffuse radiation intensity,
measured in cal/cm^2/min on a horizontal surface
- n is the number of hours of bright sunshine in the month
- b is the angle between the collector surface and the horizontal

Estimated energy that could be collected:

Of the total energy received, part will be reflected from the collector,
part will be absorbed in the glass covering and part will be lost as heat
by re-radiation from the collector both to the outside and inside. For
these reasons a value of 40% of the total energy received during periods
of bright sunshine is taken to find the total energy collected. This value
corresponds with experimental values of collector efficiency.

Table 1   Total energy collected (kWh)

JAN	FEB	MAR	APR	MAY	JUN	JUL	AUG	SEP	OCT	NOV	DEC
56.2	131.9	328.4	614.3	883.3	1036.4	758.0	729.4	413.6	223.8	78.4	42.4

From these results, it would appear that the collector described above
could provide hot water for two people throughout the summer (100
litres of hot water corresponds to an energy input of about 5 kWh a day).
If less hot water were used by substituting a shower for a bath, the
collector could provide hot water all the year through. However,
sufficient insulated storage would have to be provided to ensure hot
water during days without bright sunshine.

Table 2 Collectable solar energy throughout the year

	Total number of hours of bright sunshine	Average intensity of direct solar radiation on days of high radiation* $cal/cm^2/min$	Monthly direct solar energy collected kWh
JAN	43	0.41	105.9
FEB	63	0.49	228.5
MAR	110	0.62	577.7
APR	170	0.65	1040.0
MAY	199	0.76	1488.0
JUN	220	0.77	1728.2
JUL	193	0.63	1196.3
AUG	190	0.71	1269.5
SEP	137	0.63	731.1
OCT	96	0.57	405.0
NOV	55	0.46	151.9
DEC	40	0.41	85.9

*   The values used are averages of the Kew figures for each hour of the day. The measurements are in $cal/cm^2/min$ on a surface normal to the incoming radiation. Days of high radiation (about 8% of all days) have unclouded sky and good visibility. They bear a close relationship to days of bright sunshine, which the Campbell Stokes recorder traces, recording sunshine above $0.2 \, cal/cm^2/min$.

Solar altitude	Background diffuse radiation intensity in cal/cm^2/min**	Monthly indirect energy collected kWh	Total collectable energy received kWh
12°	0.08	34.6	140.5
22°	0.16	101.3	329.8
31°	0.22	243.3	821.0
41°	0.29	495.7	1535.7
50°	0.36	720.3	2208.3
54°	0.39	862.7	2590.9
50°	0.36	698.6	1894.9
41°	0.29	554.0	1823.5
31°	0.22	303.0	1034.1
22°	0.16	154.4	559.4
12°	0.08	44.2	196.1
7°	0.05	20.0	105.9

** These values are measured in cal/cm^2/min on a horizontal surface. The values used in the calculation are interpolated from measured values at Kew but are related to the solar altitude for each month at 10.00 hours and 14.00 hours. To use the value measured at 12.00 hours would cause an over-estimation when the intensity of radiation on a given surface was calculated for a given month. The figures for monthly bright sunshine hours are not available in enough detail for the time of day of the occurrence of a given hour of bright sunshine to be known, hence an average value for the solar altitude (i.e. 10.00 – 14.00 hours) will give a closer approximation to the altitude of the sun in any given hour than the noon altitude value.

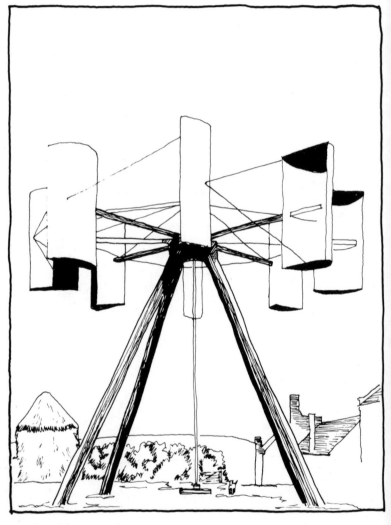

35   *A very large vertical-axis wind-powered generator built in Scotland at the beginning of this century.*

3 Harnessing the wind

Although the total energy contained in the winds blowing around the
earth could in no way match the present levels of energy demand
(Putnam, 1953), the conversion of wind power to electricity is more
economical than the direct conversion of solar energy. Therefore, even
though all winds are derived from solar energy falling on the earth and
producing convection currents, the wind is considered as a separate
source of energy for the design of autonomous systems. The wind can
be harnessed to provide direct mechanical energy, as for pumping and
grinding, or it can be made to turn a generator to give electricity.
However, despite much research into wind generators, this latter
process has remained relatively inefficient and expensive. The need for
electricity should therefore be considered carefully.

With present energy consumption in housing, electricity is used for
one or all of the following purposes: lighting, running domestic
appliances, space heating and water heating. Unless autonomy is
achieved through the use of one very large, expensive wind generator,
which is a possibility considered later, then space heating or water
heating by electricity produced by the wind is probably eliminated.
Perhaps some domestic appliances could be replaced by hand machinery,
for example the vacuum cleaner by a carpet sweeper or brush, and the
spin-drier by a mangle, leaving only the essentials of refrigeration and
lighting. Even electric lighting might be replaced by tallow lamps made
of animal fats, but more land would then be required for raising the
stock for this purpose; it might take four years for one colony of bees
to produce enough wax for one candle. Papanek (1972) has a design
for a hand-powered 'cool box' which, together with an old-fashioned
insect-proof larder, might well replace the refrigerator as we know it.
It would thus be possible to live without electricity. However, adequate
lighting can be achieved at the expense of little energy with efficient
fluorescent fittings replacing the conventional tungsten ones, which are
only 10 per cent efficient in producing light from electricity. The total
weekly power consumption of some domestic appliances is quite low;
an 800-W iron might be used once a week for two hours, giving a weekly

use of 1.6 kWh. However, trouble may be caused when this amount of power is withdrawn in a very short time, unless some type of on-line supply could be fitted and the ironing left to a windy day. Simply placing the refrigerator in a cold outside wall rather than in a heated kitchen would improve its efficiency. Provided the idea of a windmill in the backyard can be tolerated, then a small generator could be used to supply the reduced electrical needs of the house.

Apart from the generation of electricity, wind power has a long history of use; the first mills in Britain were built in the twelfth century, and the use of windmills for grinding corn and working drainage pumps has continued well into the twentieth century. First attempts at generating electricity from the wind were made at the beginning of the twentieth century and even now, after the programme of rural electrification, there are still a few houses in remote country areas where the sole source of power for a reduced demand comes from the wind. A typical installation might be a windmill of 2 metres' diameter mounted on a telegraph pole, driving a 200-W generator which would power lights, radio and television. However, machines capable of generating considerably more power have been built in other countries, for example the windmills for stations in the Australian outback. Even in the district of Cambridge, which has a fairly low average wind speed of 5 m/sec (Beaufort scale 4, a 'moderate breeze'), such a windmill, with a blade approximately 4 m in diameter driving a 2-kW generator, would give over 3,000 kWh a year, i.e. 3,000 units a year. This would be enough power for lights, radio, television, stereo, electric iron, electric kettle, spin-drier, vacuum cleaner and similar demands, but not enough for electric water heating or space heating. An 'all electric' house was actually set up in Scotland by the Electrical Research Association in the late 1950s, with power supplied for all needs, including electric storage heaters and farm equipment, by an 8-kW German windmill. The windmill itself was a very sophisticated and expensive piece of equipment, but the experiment was successful and showed that the 'free' power of the wind could be used to run a farm if one were prepared to pay for the equipment to make this possible.

Although a windmill attached to each house could provide electricity for everyone independently of fossil fuels, the visual problems implicit in the idea have caused much research to be directed to the design of large-scale mills situated in windy places and feeding power directly into the National Grid. Research was done by the Electrical Research Association after the war on the construction of large-scale wind power stations with blade diameters of 60 m or so. These were to be installed in very windy areas such as the Hebrides or the tops of certain Welsh mountains, but were eventually abandoned in favour of the cheaper and more plentiful nuclear power. The largest wind-power installation to be built was in the USA, at Grandpa's Knob in Vermont, where a 1,250-kW unit was tested during the second world war. It worked successfully for 3½ years, generating a maximum of 1,500 kW, before being shut down for repairs from 1943 to 1945. Despite the fact that it had withstood winds of up to 51 m/sec, it was realized that the supporting spars for the main blades were wrongly designed and likely to fail. As it was impossible to rectify the situation, the machine was reassembled and run, but shortly afterwards a spar broke and the blade flew off, so the work was discontinued.

One disadvantage of windmills on this scale is that the supply of power is intermittent. Moreover, being on the National Grid, they are affected by the 20 per cent transmission losses which are an inherent feature of long-distance electricity transmission. If much smaller wind-mills at a house or village scale were used, the periods of low wind speed could be catered for by batteries (which would be prohibitively expensive for a large windmill). The fact that there were a number of generators over a large area would mean that better use would be made of the available wind, as the wind at one particular site would not have to be relied on to supply power to a large number of consumers in different localities.

The wind speed is the major factor in assessing the amount of energy available at a given site, because the energy in the wind is proportional to the cube of its speed. Being an island, Britain is favourably situated for the use of wind power, as the sea offers little resistance to the passage of wind, and yet the country is large enough to cause noticeable differences in average wind speeds at different locations. Generally, coastal areas are more suitable than inland areas, and hilltops are more suitable than valleys or flat ground. The ideal site is a smoothly rounded hilltop standing in relative isolation, as this will increase the wind speed due to aerodynamic funnelling effects (see fig. 36).

The availability of wind throughout the year is such that the average wind speed in winter is about 30 per cent greater than in summer, thus giving a potential of twice as much power in the winter when it is most needed. The total amount of wind passing a point regardless of its speed (i.e. the run of wind) varies by no more than 10 per cent from one year to another, which makes it a reliable source of power as there is unlikely to be a year with very much less wind than is expected. The energy in the wind reaches a peak shortly after noon each day and is at its minimum at midnight (see fig. 37). This too is convenient, because the demands for energy in a house follow a similar pattern.

A windmill operates by reducing the velocity of the wind passing through it. Obviously, the mill cannot take all the energy from the wind,

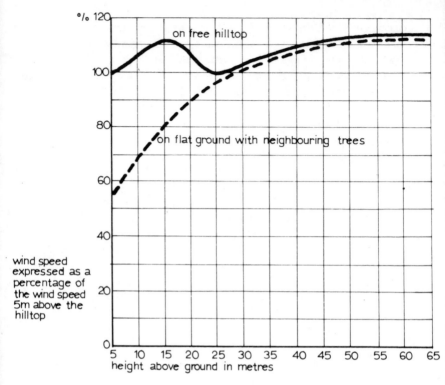

36 Variation of wind speed with height above ground (after Golding, 1955).

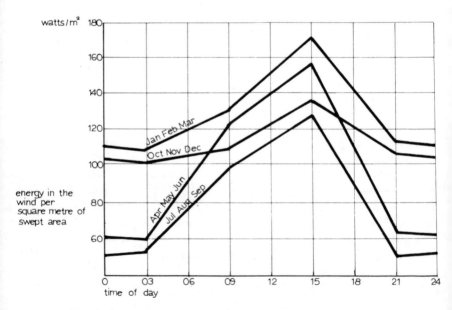

37 Daily variation of energy in the wind.

for it would not be able to escape from the machine. The energy that can be extracted by a windmill is theoretically 59.3 per cent of the total energy in the wind, but in reality only 60 per cent of this theoretical maximum will be obtained. The power that can be obtained from a given wind speed depends on the area of the surface presented to the wind. This is termed the 'swept area' of the windmill. In a traditional windmill of the type used for grinding corn, the swept area is the area of the circle described by the blades.

Before discussing the various types of windmill that are associated with pumping or electricity generation, it is worth considering some of the more unusual suggestions for obtaining power from the wind. One idea (D. Stabb) is to use a large kite fitted with spoilers which would cause it to stall, wind in its line with a counterweight mechanism, and then climb, pulling on the tethering line and operating a ratchet device to work a generator. The advantage of the system is that it would allow the use of winds at higher altitudes where there would be no disturbance from surrounding obstructions. A similar and perhaps simpler proposal is based on the child's familiar toy plane, which has wings rotating on a horizontal axle to keep it up when flown on a string like a kite. A large device of this sort could be flown on an endless tethering line, which would drive a generator. The disadvantage of both these systems, apart from the limitations imposed by the safety requirements of air traffic control, is that, when the wind drops, the device will fall to earth a long way from its point of operation, thus necessitating fail-safe retrieval devices to reel the kite in before the wind drops completely. Adding extra mechanical devices to the system will probably increase the likelihood of failure of some part as well as the initial cost. Another proposed system, which has the advantages of being ground-based and automatic in operation, is the possible use of the movements of large trees to provide power. Branches could be linked up with cables to work pumps or similar devices by means of a ratchet mechanism. Measurements have been made by students from Brunel University and the Architectural Association of the movements of tree branches in winds, and a small test installation has been operated. A 30-m-high tree would be well placed to receive a large amount of wind energy, and would cut out the problem of obtaining planning permission on a 30 m steel tower for a windmill. However, although this system has the potential to solve the visual problem of electrical generation from the wind, it is limited to people who already have large trees available, or who are prepared to wait 100 years for a suitable tree to grow.

The more conventional windmills can be divided into two main types, which are distinguished by the position of the main shaft of the machine. The first windmills, used in China 2,500 years ago, were of

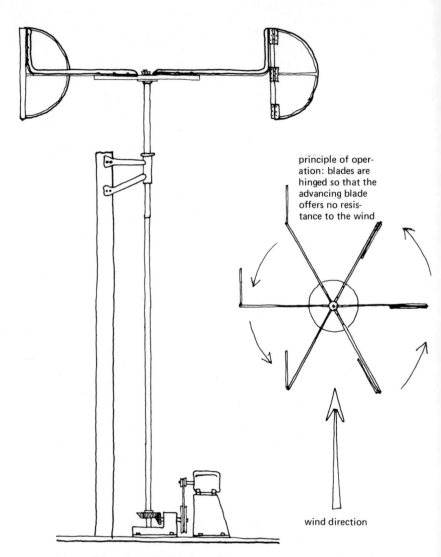

principle of oper-
ation: blades are
hinged so that the
advancing blade
offers no resis-
tance to the wind

wind direction

*38   A French design for a vertical-axis wind-powered generator in which the
blades are hinged, so that the advancing blades offer no resistance to the wind.*

the vertical-axis type, also called panemones. The familiar anemometer
for measuring wind speed is a simple machine of this type. The panemones rely either on the differing resistances to the wind of the inner
and outer surfaces of semi-cylindrical blades (as in the cup anemometer),
or on a system which turns the blade approaching the wind so that its
edge is presented to the wind, while the blade being acted on by the
wind presents its full surface area (see fig. 38). The first major improve-

ment in vertical-axis mill design was made by the Finnish designer Savonius, who designed the rotor system named after him. This consists of a bisected cylinder with the two halves displaced (see fig. 39); it works in a similar way to the anemometer type, but in addition the wind causes a lowering of pressure on the downstream side of the rotor which augments the turning force produced by the differing resistances of the two surfaces. Following tests, the Brace Research Institute of Canada found that 'area for area the Savonius rotor is about half as efficient as a multi-bladed fan mill' (a traditional farm wind pump).

The main advantage of vertical-axis machines is that they can be built cheaply and simply. However, the one panemone available on the market, from Elektro, a Swiss firm, is in fact more expensive than a horizontal machine of equivalent power (see fig. 40). This can probably

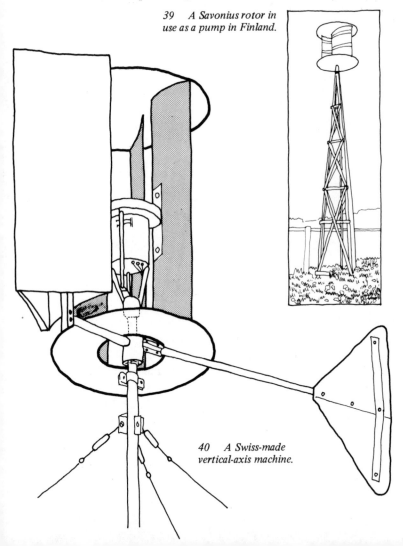

39   *A Savonius rotor in use as a pump in Finland.*

40   *A Swiss-made vertical-axis machine.*

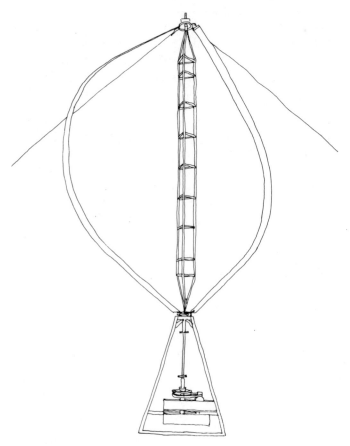

41   The 4.3 m-diameter high-speed vertical-axis windmill (after South and Rangi, 1972).

be attributed to the need for the machine to withstand high speeds and icy conditions in mountainous regions. The anemometer- and Savonius-type machines have the benefit of self-governing action. As the wind speed increases on the driven blade, it also increases on the blade coming into the wind, and thus overspeeding is automatically prevented without the need for any complicated governing mechanism. The other great advantage of all vertical-axis machines is that they need no orientation to turn them into the wind, as they can be operated by a wind from any direction.

   Another vertical-axis machine which might be more applicable to the direct generation of electricity from the wind has been developed by the National Research Council of Canada (see fig. 41). Since it has many of the characteristics of a horizontal machine, it will be described in conjunction with them. Although the Savonius rotor did improve upon the efficiency of a simple vertical-axis sail mill, its velocity ratio (rotor rotational tip speed:wind speed) remained low and could be exceeded by the more expensive horizontal-axis machine.

The other main type of windmill mentioned above is the horizontal-axis machine, typified by the traditional corn-grinding mill. The first mills of this type appeared in Britain in the twelfth century and reached a considerable degree of sophistication by the mid-nineteenth century, when steam power began to replace them. Windmill development for the raising of water from wells on the prairies in the USA began during the latter half of the nineteenth century. These mills were usually made of galvanized sheet iron and were of a high-solidity type (that is, the swept area was largely filled with blades), whereas the European grinding mills were of a low-solidity type with normally only four blades. The high-solidity multi-bladed type of windmill can achieve good power coefficients at low wind speeds and has a high starting torque which is ideal for operating a pump.

These mills have a low tip-speed ratio: the tips of the blades travel at a speed equal to or only slightly greater than the wind speed, and consequently the speed of revolution of the shaft is low. If a windmill is required to operate an electricity generator, the rotational speed of the mill must be as high as possible. Generators, even if specially

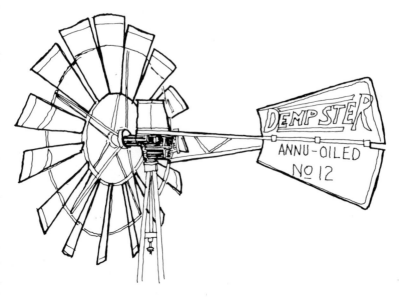

42   A multi-bladed water-pumping windmill.

designed for low-speed operation, have to turn at higher speeds than can be obtained from a high-solidity windmill. This has led to the design of special 'aerogenerators' with two or three blades of aerofoil section, which can reach tip-speed ratios of at least 6 and can be used to drive a generator directly without the need for expensive step-up gearing.

Low-speed generators for direct coupling to windmills are expensive and unwieldy, as a windmill does not often exceed 300 r.p.m. Most manufactured windmills compromise on the efficiency lost when these lower speeds are geared up to a conventional generator operating at 1,800 – 5,000 r.p.m. by selecting a generator operating at about 1,000 r.p.m. and using a small transmission of approximately 5:1 to gear the blade to the generator. Aerogenerator blades are also able to extract more power from the wind than the other types of windmills. Fig. 43 shows the relative effectiveness of four types of windmill. The disadvantage of the aerofoil-bladed machines is that they have a low starting torque, and must be carefully designed to minimize rotational friction in order to make use of low wind speeds.

A problem with all horizontal-axis windmills is that they must be governed to prevent damage by winds higher than the rated speed of the mill. The governing can be carried out in several ways. Most of the

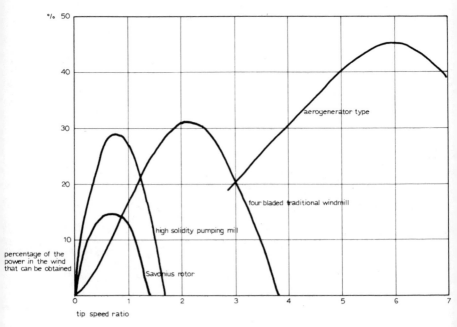

43   Power characteristics of various wind machines (Brace Institute).

74

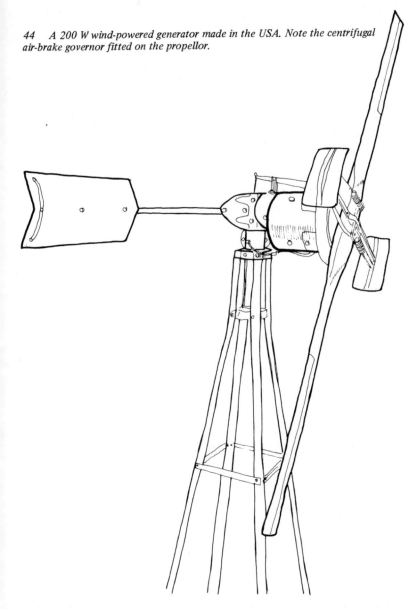

high-solidity pumping mills and a few of the smaller aerogenerators have a spring-loading arrangement which starts to turn them out of the wind when its speed increases above a certain predetermined value. The wind then strikes the blades at an angle, its effective speed is reduced, and damage is avoided. The mill can be turned at 90° to the wind by a handle when required so that maintenance can be carried out without danger from rotating blades. Another type of small aerogenerator uses a spring-loaded air brake system which prevents the propeller from turning above a certain speed. The air brake has two flat paddles which are operated by centrifugal force when the rotational speed reaches the desired value. The majority of aerogenerators use a system of blade pitch control for governing, usually worked by weights and springs. This system ensures that the angle of the blades to the wind is constantly adjusted to control the rotational speed and prevent damage to the windmill.

The action of governing means that in periods of high wind much power is wasted because the mill cannot use it. To overcome this problem, a proposal has been made to absorb surplus power with a compressor. A large-diameter, low-solidity mill would be used to drive a small generator. Once the generator was giving maximum power (this would be at a relatively low wind speed because the mill would be oversized in relation to the generator), an electromagnetic clutch would be engaged to connect the mill shaft to a compressor. The compressor would be used to operate a heat pump for heating a house (see Chapter 4). The advantage of this system is that, because of the characteristics of compressors, the compressor could be used to absorb the surplus power without the need for governing. However, problems might occur in running a heat-pump compressor at variable speeds. Such a machine has not yet been constructed, but it could well prove to be a very efficient use of the windmill, given a method of storing heat when the heat pump was not operating.

Various electricity-generating windmills available are shown in figs. 46 − 48. Most have a similar form of a propeller-type blade connected through a small step-up gear to the generator, with a tail to guide the machine into the wind. The machines are usually fairly precisely manufactured instruments and, as can be seen from the graph, are expensive to buy. However, apart from do-it-yourself designs, some research has been done into reducing the cost of wind generators.

The Princeton University 'sailwing' machine uses sails rather than the conventional wooden blades. Cloth sails have been used on traditional Cretan windmills, where the area presented to the wind can be varied by furling or unfurling the cloth, but the sailwing machine uses cloth to form a sail of aerofoil section. The idea of the sailwing, originally developed for boats and then aircraft, is to have a rigid leading edge, tip and root to the wing, connected by a cable around which is wrapped a dacron sail cut with a catenary trailing edge (see fig. 46). The sail then takes up the appropriate aerofoil section for the particular speed of wind. Governing is achieved by twisting the blade. It is claimed that the cost of such a sail should be about half the cost of

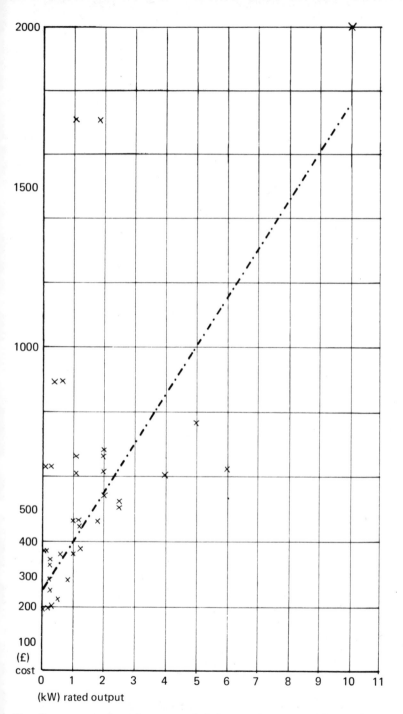

45   *Cost vs. output for various types of wind-powered generators (after Smith, 1973). The crosses represent the prices of various windmills available in 1973. (Prices exclude towers and batteries.) The chain dotted line represents an average price per kilowatt for wind generators.*

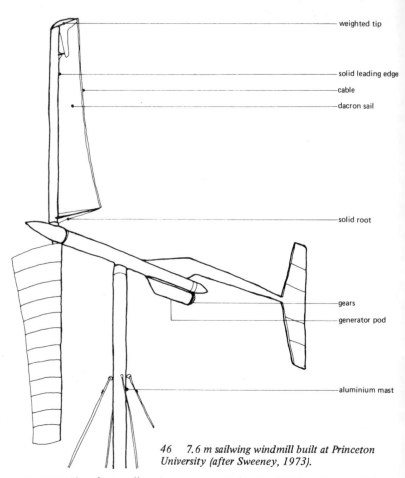

weighted tip

solid leading edge

cable

dacron sail

solid root

gears

generator pod

aluminium mast

46 *7.6 m sailwing windmill built at Princeton University (after Sweeney, 1973).*

a conventional propeller. An experimental mill of 7.6 m diameter has been constructed on this principle, with a generating capacity of 7 kW in a 9 m/sec wind. The shaft speed varies from 45 r.p.m. to 900 r.p.m., and is connected to a 7-kW aircraft generator with a 20:1 step-up gear. The same principle has been applied to a vertical-axis auto-rotating sailwing mounted on a Chrysler automotive alternator, although there is no experimental record of the machine's performance as yet.

The cost can also be reduced by making the machine simpler to construct. The vertical-axis windmill developed by the National Research Council of Canada is a very simple machine, made of two or three aerofoil blades bent into a catenary form and housed so that they can rotate about a vertical axis (see fig. 41). The aerodynamic efficiency of the machine was found to be similar to that of existing horizontal-axis machines. As with these machines, the vertical-axis windmill has to be governed to limit the maximum rotational speed and prevent high winds causing structural failure. The only problem with the rotor was its inability to start itself even when unloaded, although the negative torque is small and easily overcome to start the machine.

Plans for home-built generators have been as prolific as the generators themselves. Unlike a complete autonomous house, a generator can be constructed at a relatively small cost and put out in the back garden on a pole, without any special modification of the house structure. Much attention has, therefore, been given to the do-it-yourself windmill. From the 1920s onwards, the *LeJay Manual* published designs for wind plants, using Ford Model T generators or rewound Dodge G or GA four-pole generators to give a 32-volt DC plant.

More recently, in *Popular Science* (1972), Hans Meyer described a generator that could be built for around $200, giving about 200 W in a 4.5 m/sec wind, 1.5 kW in a 9 m/sec wind and 4.5 kW in a 13 m/sec wind. The three-bladed propeller, 3 m across, is made of expandable paper honeycomb (available from Windworks, the Wisconsin commune, of which Hans Meyer is a member), although the honeycomb core used for internal flush doors might also be a possibility. The honeycomb is cut in an aerofoil section, expanded and then covered with fibreglass. The blade is geared up to an alternator which is housed in a cowling of wood, paper and fibreglass (see fig. 47), which pivots on a Volkswagen rear wheel, hub and axle. The cowling thus orients the blades into the wind without the need for a tail. The car alternator is the cheapest generator available for home-built designs, although it needs gearing up with a ratio between 5:1 and 10:1 to correspond with the generating speeds of 2,000 – 5,000 r.p.m. For an alternator to generate current, however, the field must be energized, and if energized all the time the batteries will slowly be drained when the alternator is not charging. The field can be energized by switching the current on and off manually, or a wind-sensing switch can be fitted. Jim Sencenbaugh (1973) fitted his home-built machine with a vane dampened with a spring, which in turn operated a relay to switch on and off the 3-amp field current needed to energize the alternator. The switch can then be tuned to turn on the current at the lowest speed at which the alternator will charge. References to this and other home-built designs will be found in the bibliography (pp. 213-4).

If an aerogenerator is required to supply electricity to a house, the first step is to find the mean annual wind speed for the site in question. According to Golding's work for the Electrical Research Association, the most detailed study of wind power possibilities in Britain, the power that an aerogenerator will provide can be worked out directly

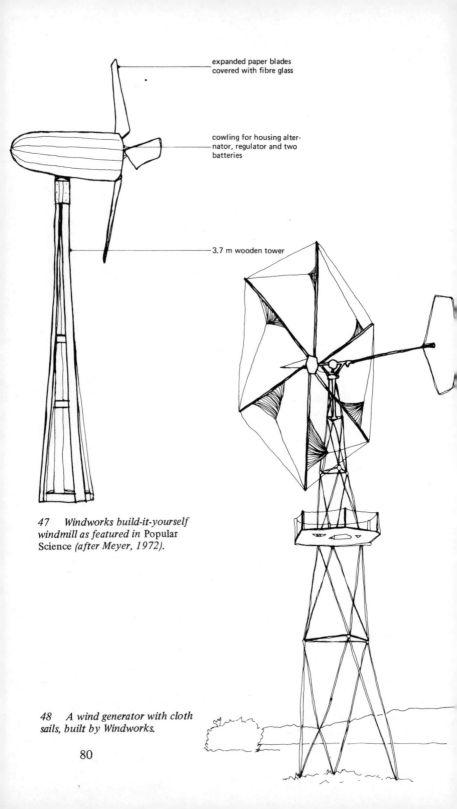

expanded paper blades
covered with fibre glass

cowling for housing alternator, regulator and two
batteries

3.7 m wooden tower

47   *Windworks build-it-yourself
windmill as featured in* Popular
Science *(after Meyer, 1972).*

48   *A wind generator with cloth
sails, built by Windworks.*

80

Traditional Cretan windmill with cloth sails.

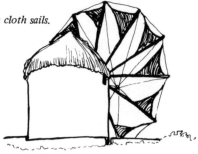

from the mean annual wind speed (see fig. 51). Studies for all parts of the country have shown that, once the mean annual speed is known, the number of hours per year of winds of various speeds can be determined and, from these, the number of kilowatt-hours that a machine of given size will supply in a year. In a wind speed of v metres/sec, a windmill of swept area a m^2 could theoretically extract 0.59 x 0.00064 x av^3 kW, but in fact a good machine will extract about 60 per cent of this theoretical maximum, or 40 per cent of the total energy in the wind.

The capacity of the aerogenerator will depend on the demand for electricity in the house. The machine must be able to meet winter demands, when more lighting is required, and should be sized with this in mind. When the yearly electricity requirement in kilowatt-hours has been worked out, the required capacity of the windmill can be read off from Golding's graph, provided the mean annual wind speed for the site is known. The graph shows two rated speeds ('rated speed' being the wind speed at which the generator gives its full output); having chosen the desired rated wind speed, one can work out the swept area of the blades by using the formula given above, bearing in mind that a 60 per cent efficiency must be allowed for. A lower rated speed requires a larger-diameter windmill, which will consequently be subjected to greater stresses and will require more careful governing. Most aerogenerators on the market have a rated wind speed of 11 m/sec. If possible, a wind-velocity duration graph for the site in question should be obtained. This shows the number of hours in the year that a wind of given velocity is blowing. If there is a noticeable flattening in the graph at any particular speed, this should be taken as the rated speed for the aerogenerator, so that the machine will deliver its maximum power for as many hours as possible. However, velocity duration curves are available for only a few Meteorological Office measuring stations, and may not therefore be obtainable for a particular site.

Ideally, the aerogenerator should be mounted well above surrounding obstructions on a tower as high as possible; 15 m would be a suitable

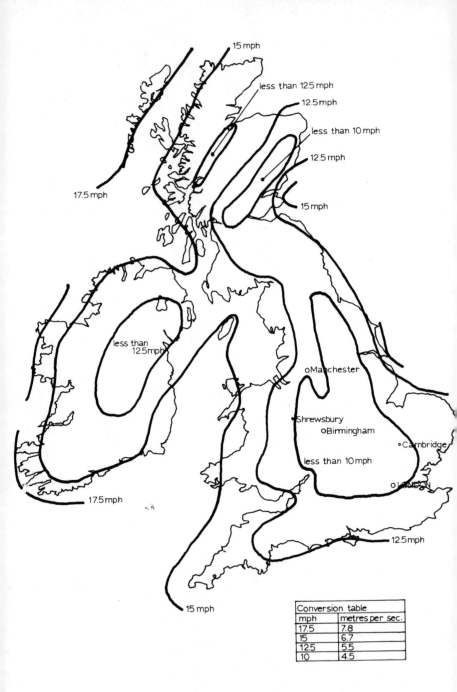

Conversion table

mph	metres per sec.
17.5	7.8
15	6.7
12.5	5.5
10	4.5

50   Isovents showing mean annual wind speed in the British Isles (after Golding, 1949).

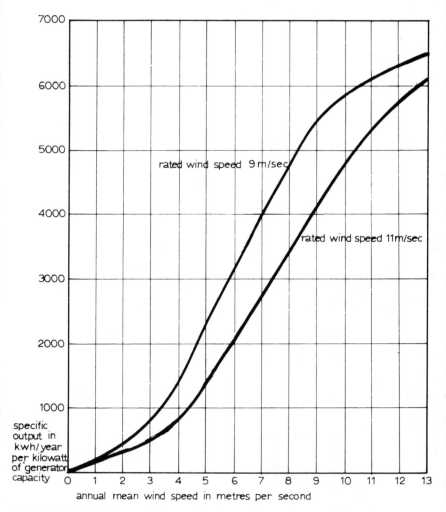

51   Relationship between wind generator output and annual mean wind speed (after Golding, 1949).

height, but often a lower tower must be used because of difficulties in obtaining planning permission. Provision should be made for climbing the tower to maintain the machine occasionally, and some sort of brake must be provided on the mill to enable maintenance to be carried out safely. It is not advisable to mount the generator on a house roof, because the unavoidable vibrations from the machine will be transmitted through the house. An engineer who used to instal small aerogenerators on holiday bungalows said that, when people specified

83

52   A well-sited wind-powered generator.

this type of mounting, they often found the vibration so bad that they stopped using the windmill and relied on paraffin lamps instead.

Some attempt should be made to discover the number of days on which the wind will be too low to generate any power. This will determine the amount of energy storage that must be provided to carry the electrical load when the wind is not blowing; the capacity should equal the number of windless days multiplied by the daily electrical power requirements in kilowatt-hours (or watt-hours if the loads are small). The only successful form of energy storage for aerogenerators is the electric storage battery. Other suggested methods, such as pumping water into a tank and allowing it to fall through a turbine when power is required, or winding up weights and allowing them to drop and turn a shaft, are simply not practical. For example, a storage capacity of 15 kWh would require 520 m^3 of water (520,000 kg) falling through 20 m (assuming an efficiency of 50 per cent for the turbine and generator system). To give a storage of 0.75 kWh, a weight of 30 tonnes would have to fall through 18 m (assuming an over-all efficiency of 50 per cent) in one hour. Two such weights would be needed, so that one was being raised by the windmill while the other was falling to provide power. Storage batteries are obviously simpler to use than these systems, and batteries for simple installations can be obtained quite cheaply, in new condition, from government surplus dealers. (For more details of batteries see Chapter 7, 'Batteries and fuel cells'.)

In America, Martin Jopp has proved that autonomous living is possible using wind power alone. He builds mills at his general store in Princeton, Minnesota, and uses three machines to run his own house. The mills stand on 21-m towers, each having a blade of 4.3-m diameter linked to a generator. The generators charge up 2.5 tonnes of lead-acid batteries, and these supply current at 110 V through an inverter to run

*53   The Jopp general stores
at Princeton, Minnesota
(after Jopp, 1972).*

the refrigerator, television, washer and so on. The wind generators cost
$1,400, although no cost is given for the battery storage. The 100-kWh
storage is provided by 60 cells, each weighing from 18 to 109 kg,
occupying a space 1.5 m x 3.6 m. The initial cost of such a system, plus
the cost of replacing the storage medium after a possible life-span of
ten years, make the totally wind-powered house less attractive.

Most designs for semi-autonomous or autonomous houses have used
wind power as the source of electricity. The 'Solar wind company'
(Clews, 1973) run their electrical appliances from a Quirk's machine;
the École operation (Ortega et al., 1972) used a sophisticated Lubing's
mill to run pumps and water heaters; Reines' Integrated Life Support
Laboratory has used three reconditioned electric generating mills to
provide power for lighting, electric tools, radio, etc.; project Ouroboros
used a purpose-built mill, now patented, designed by a student.

Provided that not too much is expected from it, a wind-powered
generator can supply the electrical power for lighting and other small
loads in a house, without requiring a very large outlay of money.
Obviously, the power will not be as immediately available as mains
power, because the state of the batteries must be watched and
electricity cannot be drawn if the batteries are nearly discharged, as
this will damage them. Nevertheless, given careful use, there is no
reason why an aerogenerator system should not prove satisfactory.

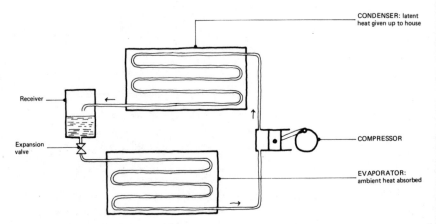

CONDENSER: latent
heat given up to house

Receiver

Expansion
valve

COMPRESSOR

EVAPORATOR:
ambient heat absorbed

54a   Vapour-compression cycle.

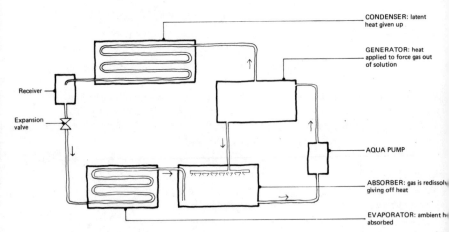

CONDENSER: latent
heat given up

GENERATOR: heat
applied to force gas out
of solution

Receiver

Expansion
valve

AQUA PUMP

ABSORBER: gas is redissolv
giving off heat

EVAPORATOR: ambient h
absorbed

54b   Vapour-absorption cycle.

4 Heat pumps

Although systems using solar energy for space and water heating have been designed, built and operated, one of the problematic points in any attempt to develop a satisfactory system is the temperature at which the air or water leaves the solar collector. For comfortable conditions in normal water-heating systems, the hot water passing through the radiators is at a higher temperature than can usually be provided by solar collectors in temperate climates. Low-temperature water-heating systems require large radiant ceiling or wall panels which have to be fitted when the building is constructed, while low-temperature air distribution systems need large areas of ducting to achieve comfortable conditions. To obtain temperatures high enough for even these low-temperature systems, collectors must be double-glazed and insulated, all of which increases their cost. At the same time, collector efficiency falls as the temperature of the water or air rises, since heat loss from the collector is increased. A system whereby it is possible to raise the temperature of a relatively large quantity of water by a few degrees and then further raise the temperature of the collected heat by a heat pump would therefore seem to have advantages over a direct solar heating system.

Observation shows that when work is put into a system, as when two sticks are rubbed together, heat is produced and the temperature of the components rises. From this observed effect a relationship can be formulated between work, heat and temperature, and this is the principle which explains the operation of the heat pump. By adding work to a large quantity of low-temperature (low-grade) heat, heat can be produced at a higher temperature (high-grade). The quantity of high-grade heat produced is greater than the heat equivalent of the work put into the system because extra energy has been transferred to the system from the low-grade source. Thus, if 1 kWh of electricity is used to operate a heat pump to upgrade the heat, 3 kWh of the high-grade heat could be produced. Although at first sight it appears that 3 kWh of heat are being gained for only 1 kWh of energy expended, this increase is achieved at the expense of the temperature of the low-grade heat source, which falls. The ratio between the high-temperature heat produced and the work put in is called the 'coefficient of performance' (COP) of the system, and this is the usual method of assessing the quality of the heat-pump system. The COP can vary from 1 to as much as 20, although values around 2.5 − 3.0 are considered normal in practice, the actual value attained depending upon conditions discussed later in this chapter. The value of the heat-pump system lies in the fact that it should theoretically be possible to extract 'heat' from the immediate surroundings by lowering the temperature of a large mass of air, soil or water by one degree or less, and to upgrade this heat, using a heat pump, so that it can be used for space and water heating in a conventional manner. As the air, water and soil are in turn heated by the sun, the system can be perpetuated.

In its most common form, the heat pump already appears in most homes as the domestic refrigerator. When the food at room temperature is placed in the refrigerator, heat is extracted from it by the heat pump until the design temperature of approximately $3° − 4°$ is reached. The motor then stops and the insulation around the refrigerator helps to maintain the low temperature inside for as long as possible, the motor only cutting in when the inside temperature rises too high. If the exhaust of the refrigerator is examined, it is evident that air is being exhausted at a temperature above room temperature. The fact that a refrigerator actually puts more heat into the kitchen than the heat equivalent of the gas or electricity used to operate it shows that the extra heat must have been gained as the food cooled from $21°$ to $4°$ C. On a much larger scale, exactly the same principle could be applied to a house. The low-grade heat could be obtained by transferring heat through coils of pipe dug into the ground or placed in the air or a watercourse, and the extra energy would most conveniently be put into the system as electricity to drive the compressor. As with the refrigerator, the better the house is insulated, the smaller are its demands for heat and the smaller the additional work that has to be done.

Like refrigerators, heat-pump systems can be run on gas or electricity, although the two systems of operation are different (see fig. 54). In the past, the electric system has been used for house heating, although some systems have been built where the compressor is driven directly by a stationary engine. The electric system, or vapour-compression-cycle heat pump, is a closed system around which a refrigerant flows. The refrigerant is a gas with a boiling-point below the temperature of a possible low-grade heat source, such as ammonia, which boils at $−33.3°$ C, or Freon 12, which boils at $−29.7°$ C. At the same time the refrigerant will condense when subjected to the pressures produced by a small electric compressor, i.e. slightly below 15,700 kN/m^2 at a temperature suitable for house heating. The refrigerant also has a high latent heat, so that it absorbs as much heat as possible in the evaporator coils when changing from a liquid to a gas.

In the heat-pump system, the first step is to compress the refrigerant gas at the temperature of the low-grade source, which is where work is put into the system. Increasing the pressure of the gas raises its boiling-point to slightly above the temperature of the high-grade heat required. The pressurized gas then passes through coils over which water or air is passed, which cools the gas below its boiling-point so that it condenses and gives out heat. The heat is transferred to the house-heating medium, and the liquid refrigerant is collected in a receiver. It then passes through a valve where it is made to expand, and the pressure drops. As it does so, the temperature of the liquid also falls. The liquid, which is now colder than the low-grade heat source, passes through the evaporator coils where the low-grade heat is absorbed as the liquid refrigerant changes to the gaseous state. From here it passes back to the compressor and the cycle is repeated.

A gas refrigerator, or vapour-absorption-cycle heat pump, works on the same principle. The gaseous refrigerant is first absorbed into a suitable solvent, such as water if ammonia is used, and in this liquid state the pressure can be raised to the required level by a very small pump or a simple percolating action. The temperature of the solution is then raised by the application of heat, such as a gas flame, at which point the refrigerant boils out of the solvent and enters the condenser as a gas. From then on the system is the same as for the vapour-compression cycle, as, after absorbing the low-grade heat in the evaporator, the gas is redissolved in the absorption fluid.

Since the heat pump has proved so successful for refrigerating food, the question arises as to why it has not been used for house heating on a large scale. More heat could be produced for the same amount of electricity, at the expense of the low-grade heat source, than if the same electricity were to be used for conventional off-peak storage or under-floor heating systems. The heat-pump system was first proposed by Lord Kelvin in 1852 in his article 'On the economy of the heating and cooling of buildings by means of currents of air', but no real exploitation of the principle was carried out for another fifty years. Even then, the heat-pump system was developed as an air-conditioner rather than a home heater. As can be seen from the diagrams of the systems, cooling can be achieved by absorbing heat from inside the house and exhausting it to the air outside through the condenser coils. For heating, the condenser coils are within the building and the evaporator coils are in contact with the low-grade heat source outside, whereas for cooling the condenser coils are outside and the evaporator coils inside. The package air-conditioner has enjoyed widespread success in America, to such an extent that the power supplies are put in jeopardy when everyone switches on during a heatwave. The use of the heat-pump cycle for cooling is mechanically easier to achieve, and the slow advance in the use of the heat-pump cycle for domestic heating can be attributed to engineering difficulties. In cold winter climates the heat pump would be used for longer periods, and the frequency of switching on and off would also be greater than for a cooling unit working in summer. This additional wear on the machinery increases the chance of mechanical breakdown. In early heating systems, compressor failures were frequent and costly to repair, for the heating cycle requires a higher compression ratio than is necessary for cooling, with consequent increased internal stress. However, work carried out in the 1960s in America has improved the performance and reliability of air-to-air heat pumps, especially with regard to the compressor, so that it is now possible to purchase these units for domestic installation.

Their chief drawback at present is the high capital cost of the machine (approximately £100/kW), although in America part of this cost is offset by the fact that the machine can be used both for heating in winter and for cooling in summer. It is doubtful whether air-conditioning is really necessary in summer in Britain. The air-to-air heating cycle would also be difficult to operate in Britain as the relative humidity of the air is generally higher than in America. As the outside temperature drops to around 0° C, frost tends to form on the evaporator coils as the heat is absorbed from the air surrounding them. This frost reduces the rate of heat transfer between the air and the refrigerant. The efficiency of the system is reduced since some means of defrosting the coils must be found, and this is normally achieved by reversing the cycle so that the outside coil becomes the condenser for the time taken to defrost it. From this evidence, it would seem that the use of air-to-air package heat pumps is not as attractive in Britain as in America. Nevertheless, if the soil were used as the low-temperature source, or a body of water where this is available, some of these problems could be overcome. If electricity were at such a premium that its conservation was important, then the capital cost of the heat pump would weigh less against its installation and this method of space heating would become more attractive.

There is one further problem which limits the efficiency of the heat pump and bears directly on its use as a domestic unit. The COP of the perfect heat-pump system is defined as the ratio between the absolute temperature (in $^\circ$ Kelvin) at which the heat is exhausted and the difference between this temperature and the absolute temperature at which the low-grade heat is absorbed, this difference corresponding to the work put into the system. From the table on p. 107 giving the COP of an ideal heat pump operating between T_1 and T_2, it can be seen that, for the COP to be the maximum possible, the difference between the two operating temperatures must be as small as possible and the lower temperature as high as possible. Since it is not possible to change the lower temperature, which is fixed by the ambient conditions, except possibly by using solar-heated water of above ambient temperature, the higher temperature should be as low as possible if the system is to be efficient. Thus hot-water radiators, which require water at 74° C, would have to be replaced with low-temperature radiant panels, which use water at 46° C, or ducted warm-air systems, which can operate as low as 30° C.

Even so, these ideal COPs cannot be achieved in practice because of the mechanics of the system. A temperature gradient must exist between the temperature of the refrigerant and both that of the water cooling the condenser and the low-grade source around the evaporator, so that heat transfer takes place. This means that the refrigerant temperature is $5^\circ - 10^\circ$ C above that of the water or air used for heating, and also $5^\circ - 10^\circ$ C below that of the low-temperature source. The theoretical values also depend on the compression and expansion of the gas taking place isothermally, which means that the temperature of the refrigerant is assumed to remain constant when the gas is compressed or expanded through the valve. This cannot be achieved in practice.

Power is also necessary to drive the heat-transfer medium over the condenser coils, and using a fan to drive air over the coils may take an equivalent of 10 per cent of the total energy input. Lastly, the compressor can never be 100 per cent efficient. If electrically driven, its efficiency could be $85 - 90$ per cent, but this would be reduced if the compressor were diesel-driven.* Thus the COP that can be achieved in practice will be about 30 per cent of the theoretical values shown in the table. Because of this discrepancy between the theoretical and obtainable values, the performance of a heat-pump system is measured by its performance/energy ratio (p.e.r.), which is the ratio of the heat output at T_1 to the input to the heat-engine system. In this way all local inefficiencies are taken account of.

Despite the limitations of the heat-pump system, units have been built and operated in Britain. The Electrical Research Association installed a heat pump in a laboratory building at Shinfield near Reading,

* If, however, the diesel engine were fitted with a waste-heat boiler for an additional capital cost, the effective performance/energy ratio would be about twice that of an electrically-driven heat pump (Griffiths, 1956).

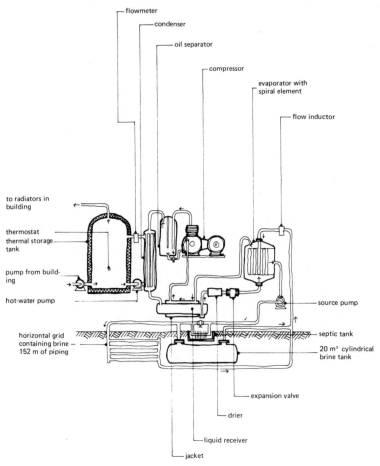

55   Diagram of heat-pump installation at Shinfield (after Griffiths, 1956).

Berkshire, in 1951, in order to gain experience in heat-pump operation,
The building was heated with pressed steel panel radiators, the water
circulating at 49° C, and the soil was used as the source of low-grade
heat, the rate at which heat was taken from the ground being 16 — 20
kW. A 7.5-kW electrically-driven compressor produced a maximum
working design pressure of 1,380 kN/m². The refrigerant used was Freon
12, which was condensing at a design temperature of 54° C. The
expansion valve produced a pressure drop from 1,170 kN/m² to
140 kN/m². The other components of the system are shown in the
diagram. Brine was used as the circulating fluid between the evaporator

and the coils in the earth, being driven with a 0.6-kW circulating pump. Calcium chloride was later added to the brine to lower its freezing-point, because freezing had begun to occur as the soil temperature dropped. From earlier experiments on the heat flow from clay soils to copper pipes, it was calculated that the required heat-flow rate would be achieved with 610 m of copper pipe 19 mm in diameter, this diameter having proved optimal during the experiments. However, this length of pipe run could not be accommodated on the site and so the chief low-temperature heat source was a 20.4-m^3 tank of brine, which was combined with 152 m of galvanized iron pipe buried horizontally 1 m beneath the lawn, the pipes being spaced 0.3 m apart in a grid. A portion of the circulating brine was also passed through a small coil in a septic tank. Although the temperature of the ground fell as heat was extracted from it during the winter months, it had regained the same temperature as undisturbed ground at a depth of 1 m by the middle of the following August. The system ran successfully for at least ten years, and the reported maintenance in the first four years of operation was very light. The heat pump was able to maintain the design conditions within the laboratory, except for a period at the beginning when the brine froze at the circulating fluid outlet. Table 3 on p.106 shows the performance of the heat pump and the rate of collection from the low-grade heat source. The p.e.r. of the system varied from 4 at the beginning to under 3 as the temperature of the soil dropped.

In 1954 the subject of a heating system for Nuffield College, Oxford, came under discussion, and an experimental heat-pump installation was chosen to provide one-third of the heating load of the college. As there was no suitable watercourse near by and the ground space for coils was limited, an air-source heat pump was first considered. The problem of handling large quantities of air and the noise associated with this prevented the exploitation of this source, and an arrangement was eventually made for the college to tap into a local sewer and extract heat from the sewage for a nominal rent of £5 a year. As the sewer was some distance from the college, it was decided to place the heat pump next to the sewer and pump the hot water to the college. Fig.56 shows the over-all heat-pump system. Three types of heating are used in the college, namely built-in panels for water at 49° C, low-temperature radiators at 60° C and normal radiators at 71° C. These are all connected to the college boiler system and the heat-pump loop through a three-way mixing valve, so that different quantities of water can be withdrawn from the boiler and the heat-pump system according to the outside temperature. The compressor in the heat-pump loop is driven by a diesel engine, and the refrigerant used is water. Heat is absorbed from the sewage at 11° C and condensed at 43° C. The waste heat from the

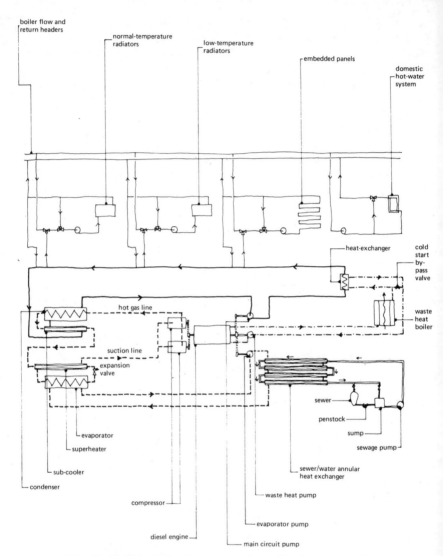

56   The Nuffield College heat pump (after Kell and Martin, 1963).

diesel engine is also used as a heat source, being upgraded, passed through a heat exchanger and then returned to the jacket round the boiler. The theoretical COP of the system is 6.9, but this would be reduced in practice because of inefficiencies within the system. The p.e.r. appears to be approximately 1.5. The Nuffield heat pump is still in operation, although it had to undergo repairs during its working life.

94

In the early 1950s, one or two heat-pump units were marketed. These were designed to be installed in the larder, from which the heat was extracted, and then upgraded to supply hot water to the house. The Brentford Duotherm unit of this type, shown in fig. 57, was designed to provide 546 litres of water per day at 60° C. The unit consisted of a refrigerator with a capacity of about 0.07 m³, together with provision for cooling of the pantry where it was installed. A fan in the unit circulated the larder air so that uniform cooling was achieved. Another important part of the unit was the radiator fitted in an airing cupboard. The hot water for the radiator was supplied by the heat-pump unit, with the flow controlled by an automatic valve. The radiator helped to maintain uniform operating efficiency despite wide load fluctuations, and was thus an essential component of the system. The hot-water tank was an insulated copper cylinder housed within the unit. The total load taken by the unit was approximately 350 W. Its initial performance was rather disappointing although further improvements, such as recovering the waste heat of the motor compressor unit, gave a p.e.r. of between 2 and 3. However, the chief reason for the failure of the units to sell well was that they were classed as refrigerators rather than heaters and therefore carried purchase tax, which meant that they were not competitive with simple immersion heaters, although they made more efficient use of the electricity.

A further experiment in the late 1950s was the installation by a building development company of a heat-pump heating system in new housing in Berkshire. The unit was an air-to-air type made of standard refrigerating and ventilating components. The main evaporator coils were mounted at the top of a cupboard in the larder, with a built-in ice-box underneath. An auxiliary evaporator was situated in the garage. The 750-watt compressor and the condenser were housed in a single unit under the stairs. A small fan was also incorporated to blow air over the condenser coils, the heat being distributed to the house through air ducts. It was claimed that 4 kW of heat were produced for 1 kW of electricity and in very cold weather a 3-kW element included in the air circuit would be turned on thermostatically to boost the air temperature. A 'same-day maintenance service' was promised with the sale of the heat-pump-heated houses, but there is no record of their actual performance over a number of years.

To overcome the problem of the difference between source temperature and required temperature, some houses were built and tested in Keadby, Yorkshire, which used waste heat from a nearby power station as the low-temperature source for a small heat pump. The six houses were well insulated, the walls having a U-value of 0.6 W/m²degC, about three times the then standard value (1.7 W/m² degC)

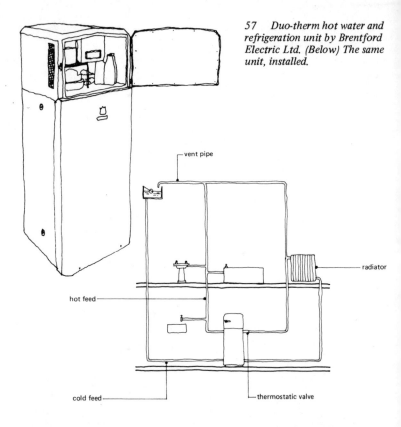

57 *Duo-therm hot water and refrigeration unit by Brentford Electric Ltd. (Below) The same unit, installed.*

vent pipe

radiator

hot feed

cold feed

thermostatic valve

for a normal 280-mm brick cavity wall. A 500-watt electric heat pump was used, and heat was taken from both power-station cooling water and the larder air. Air was used to distribute the heat around the house. However, the scheme was never really followed up, as the high initial cost of the one-off scheme had made the whole project uneconomic, especially when it was compared with simple district-heating schemes for houses near power stations which were heated with bled steam.

One or two private individuals have installed, and some are still using, heat pumps in their own houses. Fig. 58 shows the outward form of the Denco Miller package heat pump installed by the architect Ed Curtis in his own home in Rickmansworth in 1957. The original unit was an air-to-air heat pump with the evaporator coils mounted on the garage roof. This supplied hot air to the house, while the hot water came from a separate heat pump linked to a refrigerator, similar to the manufactured units described above. The latter unit was discarded as it broke down frequently, and when the fan motor of the air-to-air unit broke down after two years, the system was altered and domestic cold water was used as the low-temperature heat source. This modified unit has been in operation since.

Apart from these private ventures and the attempt to instal a heat pump in the Festival Hall in London, which was to draw waste heat from the Thames, there have been few systems built in Britain recently although, as already mentioned, package air-conditioners, which are small reversible heat-pump systems using air as both the cold source

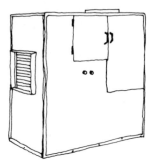

58 *The heat-pump air-conditioning unit by Denco Miller Ltd. It is about 155 cm high.*

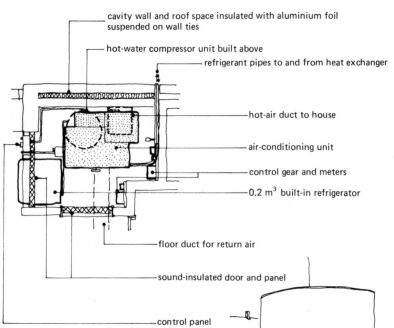

cavity wall and roof space insulated with aluminium foil suspended on wall ties

hot-water compressor unit built above

refrigerant pipes to and from heat exchanger

hot-air duct to house

air-conditioning unit

control gear and meters

0.2 m³ built-in refrigerator

floor duct for return air

sound-insulated door and panel

control panel

59 *Layout of 2 m² heat-pump room (after Curtis, 1958). (Right) Detail of air-to-air heat exchanger on garage roof of Ed Curtis's house. The pipes at the right take the refrigerant from the heat-pump room to the heat exchanger.*

and the heat sink, have found a widespread market in the USA. Westinghouse have installed one of their units of this type in a four-bedroomed house at Oxted in Surrey. The installation was under test from September 1973 to September 1974, and it is expected to show a 20 per cent saving over the conventional warm-air gas-fired system. If the air-to-air unit is, in fact, successful in operation in the British climate, it will be interesting to see whether the manufacturers find as wide a market for this form of heating in Britain as they have in America.

Any plant for heating will necessarily be larger and more complicated than a domestic refrigerator, and the heat-pump units would also be more expensive. At the same time, a wide choice of heating equipment with various capital and running costs is already on the market, and the introduction of a heat-pump system would need to show a definite economic advantage before it became competitive. Until now fuel has been comparatively cheap, and therefore systems with low capital costs and high running costs have been popular. If fuel prices increase, however, the heat-pump system, which has a very high capital cost but provides perhaps three times as much heat for the same amount of energy put in, may find favour. The mass production of such units for widespread use would also lower their initial cost, as has happened with the air-conditioning units in America.

Nevertheless, some low-temperature heat source must be found for all such installations, except in very special circumstances where heat pumps could use cooling water from power stations or even industrial plants. The problems of using air as the low-grade heat source in Britain have already been mentioned, and although the system can be reversed for a short period to defrost the coils, such a procedure lessens the over-all performance of the system. A river or stream provides the most useful source, as the flow of water means that heat can usually be extracted without any risk of freezing the watercourse. A well-insulated house could be heated from a stream with a cross-sectional area of 1,000 cm^2, flowing at 5 m/min, with a drop of only 0.5 degC in the water temperature. But even if autonomous houses were built in a decentralized way, water would not be available everywhere. The earth, however, is a good source of low-temperature heat because the temperature of the soil is relatively stable, particularly as the depth increases above 500 mm (see fig. 60). At this depth the undisturbed soil temperature is unlikely to drop below 5° C, so that there is scope for extracting heat without danger of freezing.

The actual heat-transfer characteristics of the soil depend on the ground water content, a drier soil having a lower heat conductivity than a wet soil and hence requiring a longer run of pipe for the circulating fluid. The cost of the pipe run can be high, especially if copper pipes

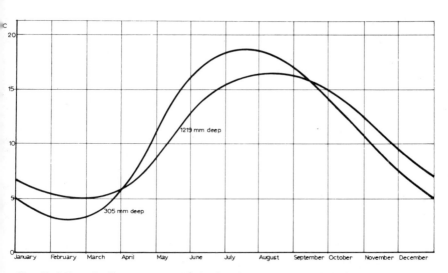

60   Variation of soil temperature with depth and season (Botanical Gardens, Cambridge, England, 1970).

are used in a dry soil, but Griffiths (1972) says that the pipe material is probably unimportant; the contact between soil and pipe is usually poor anyway, so that plastic pipe would probably be as satisfactory as copper, and much cheaper to instal. The Shinfield installation (fig. 55) used a brine and calcium chloride circulating fluid between the low-temperature heat source and the refrigerant in the evaporator, but in a smaller domestic installation built in the 1940s (Faber, 1946) which had 146 m of 25-mm copper pipe running under the house and 159 m of 25-mm pipe under the lawn, the refrigerant, Freon 12, was circulated directly through the coils. However, there was an immediate loss of the refrigerant in this system because of a failure in the pipe joints, a reaction having been established between the soil, the aluminium-bronze coupling and the copper pipe. This demonstrates that care must be taken to prevent corrosion reactions between the pipes and the circulating fluid, whether this is the refrigerant or an intermediary. Since the work was done in the 1950s the rapid development and use of plastic pipes and joints may make the construction of ground coils simpler and cheaper, especially as the heat transfer from soil to pipe is not very important. However, it should be remembered that, if refrigerant is circulating through the ground coils, the joints must be capable of withstanding the pressures involved in this side of the circuit.

The effect of lowering the temperature of the soil appears to have no adverse effect on the grass or plants growing in it. In both the Shinfield and the smaller domestic installation mentioned above, the grass areas containing the soil coils appeared convex at the end of the heating season, but the grass was not damaged. Root crops planted over the large brine tank at Shinfield grew satisfactorily.

Another possible low-temperature source for domestic installations is water from baths, washing and laundry which, once used, retains a large portion of the heat initially used to raise its temperature. Such a system has been installed in a house (Faber, 1946), using only the waste water from the bath and upstairs basin, to avoid the possibility of contamination from kitchen waste. However, this only supplied one-sixth of the total heat requirements of the house, the remainder of the low-temperature heat being extracted from the outside air. Better insulating of houses would be essential if only waste hot water were to be used, although the higher temperature of this water means that the p.e.r. would be greater than for a soil or river-water coil.

As may be seen from this and the previous examples, it is possible to make up all the necessary low-grade heat from a variety of sources. For the design of a heat pump for the Biotechnic Research and Development Group in North Wales, three sources were considered. The heat pump had to be capable of delivering 14 kW once other methods of heating the building, such as open fires and solar collectors, had been taken into consideration. A small stream was estimated to be capable of giving 4.7 kW to the evaporator coil if the temperature were lowered by 1 degC. Extracting heat from washing, bathing and laundry water fed into a holding tank would provide a further estimated 1 kW in lowering the temperature from 25° C to 5° C. The third possible source was a cold store containing a commercial deep-freeze cabinet. As the deep freeze works in exactly the same way as a conventional refrigerator, taking heat from the food and putting it out into the room, a coil placed in the cold store would utilize this heat and also increase the efficiency of the deep freeze, since the lower room temperature would mean that the rate of heat passing from the room to the freezer contents would drop and less electricity would be needed to run the freezer. However, a variety of sources increases the complexity and cost of the installation, and it would probably be better to reduce the demand for heat by better insulation than to increase the size and output of the heat pump.

The performance of the heat pump could be improved if the source of low-temperature heat were limited to solar-heated water. (As discussed earlier, solar collection is much more efficient if the water need not be raised to temperatures suitable for space heating.) Examples of domestic installations working on this principle have been built and tested in both Japan and America (see figs. 61-63). The total amount of plant is still large and complicated, and some method of distributing low-temperature heat to the home must still be found. All

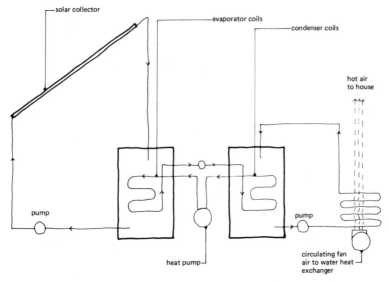

61   Solar-heated laboratory at Nagoya, Japan (after Proceedings of Conference on New Sources of Energy, *1961). The laboratory is both heated in winter and cooled in summer. For winter heating, water is heated in the unglazed black tube-in-sheet solar collector and circulates to the tank containing the evaporating coils. The heat is then upgraded by the heat pump and transferred to the tank containing the condenser coils. From here it is circulated to the heat exchanger where the heat is transferred to air blown across it and thence to the rooms. For the cooling cycle, air from the rooms is passed over the heat exchanger where it gives up its heat to the water circulating from the tank. The heat-pump action is reversed, so the heat is transferred from this tank to the tank linked to the collector. The hot water is then circulated through the collector at night, where it loses heat to the sky and is cooled ready to take up another heat load. The storage capacity of the tanks is sufficient to maintain the design temperature in the rooms for 1.3 days.*

the solar heat-pump systems can be reversed to provide summer cooling and winter heating.

The most recent development in heat-pump research is the use of the thermo-electric principle. Rather than using a thermocouple of two dissimilar metals to generate a potential difference when one end is kept cold and the other warm, electricity is supplied to the thermo-electric heat pump to produce heat at the expense of the cold end. However, work on this is still experimental with, as yet, no direct application.

The last problem of the heat-pump system in the context of an autonomous house is the need for an electricity supply to operate the compressor, as a diesel-driven system cannot be considered in view of impending fuel shortages. In earlier assessments of heat-pump perform-

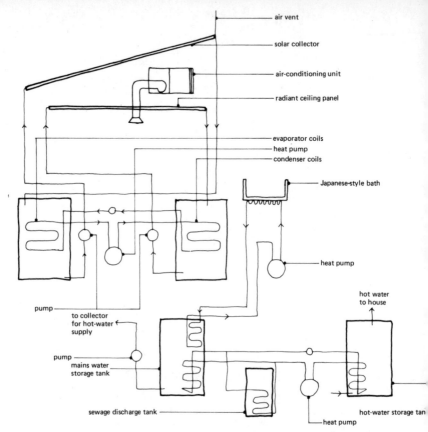

Labels on figure:
- air vent
- solar collector
- air-conditioning unit
- radiant ceiling panel
- evaporator coils
- heat pump
- condenser coils
- Japanese-style bath
- heat pump
- hot water to house
- pump
- to collector for hot-water supply
- pump
- mains water storage tank
- sewage discharge tank
- hot-water storage tank
- heat pump

62 *Solar house at Tokyo, Japan (after* Proceedings of Conference on New Sources of Energy, *1961). Apart from the basic two-tank storage system, further heat pumps are included to achieve a more comprehensive system. The main heating and cooling system has a 2.2 kW heat pump linked to two water-storage tanks. A second heat-pump system takes heat from a tank of mains water which is circulated through an area of collector on the roof, and a sewage discharge tank, and upgrades it to provide domestic hot water. A third heat-pump system takes heat from the mains water tank and upgrades it to heat a Japanese-style bath. The heating and cooling systems operate in the same way as the system in the laboratory described on p. 101, except that heat is transferred to the house through water circulating in radiant ceiling panels in winter, and in summer the cooled water is circulated through a conventional fan-coil air-conditioning unit. The collector on the roof of the house is unglazed.*

ance, a comparison was made between the direct burning of coal in domestic boilers and its conversion to electricity in the power station and subsequent use in a heat pump. Since the efficiency of conversion of coal or oil into electricity is about 40 per cent at the power station, and this efficiency drops to about 20 per cent through transmission losses

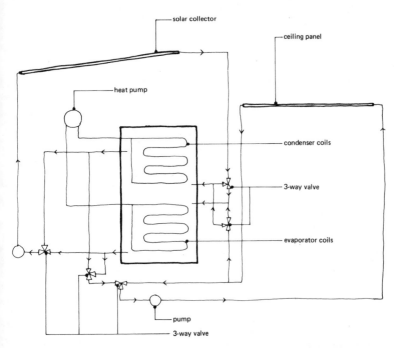

solar collector

ceiling panel

heat pump

condenser coils

3-way valve

evaporator coils

pump

3-way valve

63   Solar-heated office at Tucson, Arizona (after Proceedings of Conference on New Sources of Energy, *1961).*
The combined solar-heating and heat-pump system has a 17,055-litre storage tank. Water is used as the heat transfer medium and also for storing heat. The flat-plate copper solar collector is mounted on the roof and water is circulated through it during the day to be heated and during summer nights to be cooled. Similar panels are mounted in the ceiling of the laboratory, through which warm water is circulated in the winter and the cooled water in the summer. The storage tank is divided into two compartments although the water can flow between the two. The natural stratification of hot and cold water prevents mixing. For winter heating, water circulates between the collector and the lower part of the tank. The heat pump is used to transfer the heat from this lower part to the upper half of the tank, from where it is distributed to the ceiling panels at a higher temperature. The pumps and valves allow for different arrangements of heating and cooling cycles so that the building can be cooled in summer and alternately heated and cooled in spring and autumn.

by the time it reaches the consumer, a p.e.r. of over 3.5 must be achieved using mains electricity, as coal- or oil-fired boilers can be made with an efficiency of 65 per cent or even more (Griffiths, 1956).

   This p.e.r. limit could be lower if the rate of air change were reduced, as a low-temperature water radiator system coupled with a heat pump could be used in a house where the air infiltration could be limited and the heat loss through ventilation considerably reduced. This

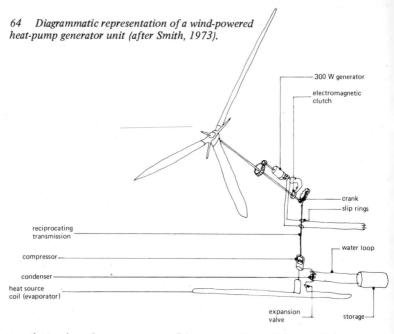

ventilation heat loss represents a large proportion of the total heat loss from a house. If coal or oil boilers are used within the house and waste heat from them is utilized, air must be fed in to provide the appliances with oxygen, and this in turn increases the number of air changes and the demand for heat, while lowering the over-all efficiency of the plant.

In the autonomous situation the use of electricity for space heating could be difficult to justify. The only possible source of electricity at this scale is wind power and, as can be seen from Chapter 3, the capital cost of wind-power plant is high, particularly for machines capable of supplying more than the basic electricity requirement (see graph, p.77). However, it might be possible to devise a system in which the generator is coupled directly to the compressor of a heat pump (see fig. 64). This system even appears to have advantages over the direct generation of electricity from the wind. The machine first drives a generator to supply the essential electrical load, and then all excess mechanical power is absorbed by the compressor, the power take-up of which is similar to the power output of the windmill as the wind speed increases. This means that there is no longer any need to govern the windmill. At the same time, lower wind speeds can be utilized, and the windmill can be given high solidity, which makes it easier to construct. However, little research into this combination has been carried out, and it is therefore not known whether the variable-speed input of the wind generator to the compressor will have any effect on the heat-pump cycle.

Where power from natural sources such as hydro-electric schemes is available, the heat-pump system has obvious advantages. In Zurich, Switzerland, in 1942-43, a district heating scheme was linked with a large heat-pump installation. Three machines capable of delivering heat to the condenser at 1.5 million kcal/hr were driven with electrical energy produced from water power, at the same time using the river as the low-temperature heat source. These machines delivered heat to the district heating scheme and a number of public buildings.

There exists a range of situations in which a heat-pump system can show a saving in fuel for some capital investment. If fuels are going to be in short supply, this is one machine that could be installed in existing houses to supply space heating, especially if extra insulation could be wrapped round the outside of the buildings. Electricity would still have to be supplied from existing power stations but, with insulation on the outside of the buildings, off-peak electricity might be used to run the heat pump during the night, the brick walls within the insulation acting as a storage radiator. The ideal low-temperature source would be a natural watercourse, such as the Thames in London; where this is not possible, the ground and possibly the waste heat contained in bath and washing water could be used. Space heating would then be achieved with a minimum of electricity put into the system, although the actual conversion of coal to electricity would still remain inefficient.

If, however, central servicing systems are not desired and autonomous servicing of houses is considered ideal, the heat-pump system has a more limited potential. Even if it is combined with low-temperature solar collectors so that the performance of the system is increased, some electricity must be introduced to drive the compressor. If a direct wind-driven compressor could be developed, especially if the machines were dual-purpose so that the necessary electricity for lighting etc. could be generated at the same time, then the heat-pump system would become a more attractive prospect, since maximum wind speed and duration, unlike maximum solar energy, occur in the winter when space heating is most needed. However, whether this system or the fitting of a heat pump into an existing house is under consideration, some method of heat distribution must be found. Experiments to date indicate an upper limit of 44° C, which necessitates low-temperature ceiling or wall-panel radiators, or large ducts for air handling. If a new house is being built the panels are probably better as they do, in fact, provide ideal comfort conditions. In an existing house, however, especially if it is well insulated, it might be best to deliver the warm air to a single point near the heat-pump condenser in the middle of the house, allowing it to infiltrate round the house from there to provide at least background heating.

One possible disadvantage of using a heat pump for space heating is the mechanical complexity of the machine, as this means that breakdowns would have to be serviced professionally. However, the package air conditioner and the domestic refrigerator have demonstrated that it is possible to design and manufacture reliable heat pumps. Mass production of domestic heating units would probably bring down the capital cost, and increasing fuel prices could revive the interest in the heat pump as a method of heating existing houses, although its use in any new autonomous situation would probably be limited to a direct wind-driven compressor plant, could such a machine be developed.

Table 3   Thermodynamic performance of the Shinfield heat pump and collection of heat from low-grade heat source (after Griffiths, 1956)

Rate of heat input to condenser kW	Rate of heat output to water kW	Electrical input to compressor kW	Work done on Freon 12 kW	Efficiency of compressor and motor %
32.1	28.6	7.65	5.6	73*
24.7	22.0	6.95	5.07	73
28.7	25.5	7.57	5.52	73
21.7	19.3	7.87	5.75	73

Condenser efficiency %	Rate of heat input to suction vapour kW	Heat taken from soil kW	Heat absorbed from room air kW+
89*	26.5	22.5	4.0
89	18.63	14.13	4.5
89	23.18	18.68	4.5
89	15.95	11.3Q	4.65

Contribution of each source of low-grade heat

main tank kW	septic tank kW	grid kW	Temperature of sources °C
22.5	—	—	4.4
8.53	1.5	4.1	−2.8
11.28(e)	2.0	5.4	−3.9
7.1	1.3	2.9	−5.6

e   estimated
*   established for one condition and assumed constant
+   estimated as the difference of columns 7 and 8

Table 4   Coefficient of performance of an ideal heat pump operating between T_1 and T_2 T_1 (°C)

T_2 (°C)	10	15	20	25	30	35	40
−25	8.1	7.2	6.5	6.0	5.5	5.1	4.8
−20	9.4	8.2	7.3	6.6	6.1	5.6	5.2
−15	11.3	9.6	8.4	7.4	6.7	6.2	5.7
−10	14.1	11.5	9.8	8.5	7.6	6.8	6.3
− 5	18.9	14.4	11.7	9.9	8.7	7.7	7.0
0	28.3	19.2	14.6	11.9	10.1	8.8	7.8
5	56.6	28.8	19.5	14.9	12.1	10.3	8.9
10	inf.	57.6	29.3	19.9	15.1	12.3	10.4

Table 5   Most probable conditions of heat pump application (after Griffiths, 1956)

Use for heat	Heat distribution medium	T_1 (°C)	source of low-grade heat	T_2 (°C)	Value of p.e.r.	
					possible	achieved
Space heating	air	32-38	air	−4	5.9	4.0
			exposed water	3	6.9	5.2
			ground water	10	8.2	5.5
			soil	0	6.5	5.0
			waste heat	21	11.5	6.0
			waste heat	27	14.1	6.0
Space heating	water	49	air	−4	5.1	3.2
			exposed water	3	5.7	4.3
			ground water	10	6.5	5.0
			soil	0	5.4	4.0
			waste heat	21	8.5	6.0
			waste heat	27	9.7	6.0
Hot water storage and utilization	water	60	air	−4	4.4	3.0
			exposed water	3	4.9	3.7
			ground water	10	5.5	4.0
			soil	0	4.7	3.5
			waste heat	21	6.7	5.0
			waste heat	27	7.3	5.5

Note The values of p.e.r. achieved probably refer to large installations. For small household-size plants the p.e.r. may be as low as half the values shown. The larder units described earlier had p.e.r. s of around 2 whereas the value from the table is given as 3.0 for air at −4° C, colder than the larder air.

5 Recycled waste

In a garden compost heap the initial mixture of grass, weeds, kitchen waste and soil, with the possible addition of manure from hens or other animals, changes over a period of time, if the heap is properly managed, into a uniform brown, crumbly peat-like substance called well-rotted compost. This transformation is achieved by the bacteria in the soil which is sometimes placed in layers in the heap between the plant wastes, or otherwise enters the compost still clinging to the roots of weeds. The bacteria feed on the vegetable matter, breaking down the complex molecules into much simpler constituents. During the process, the nitrogen contained in the plants is oxidized with the oxygen available in the air into soluble nitrates and nitrites, and the carbon to carbon dioxide. The soluble nitrites and nitrates are returned to the soil when the compost is applied, while the carbon dioxide dissipates into the atmosphere; all are to be used again in the cycle of plant life.

If, however, air is excluded from a compost heap, different bacteria, those which can live without oxygen, start breaking down the plants and manure. This situation is usually associated with the bad smells and putrefaction that can occur when a garden compost heap, especially one containing kitchen garbage, is insufficiently ventilated. As there is not enough oxygen present to complete the oxidation of the carbon and nitrogen released during decomposition, the final products include ammonia, nitrogen, methane and carbon dioxide, the first three all requiring the addition of more oxygen to complete the process of oxidation. But if methane is raised to a temperature of $345° - 400°$ C in air, it ignites and completes the process of oxidation to carbon dioxide and water as it burns in the air, at the same time evolving heat. If man could thus interrupt the process of decomposition, he could collect the methane and use it as a fuel, without finally distorting the cycle.

The process of decomposing sewage in the absence of oxygen, which is in all respects similar to decomposing a mixture of vegetable waste and manure, was first used to solve the problem of dealing with the putrescible solid matter of sewage more efficiently by breaking down approximately 80 per cent of the organic matter and destroying nearly all the harmful bacteria. On reaching the sewage works, the raw sewage passes slowly through sedimentation tanks where the solid matter settles out. After consolidation this raw sludge is pumped to a number of heated tanks (the two at Cambridge each hold 2,730 m^3 of sludge) called sludge digesters, where the decomposition or digestion takes place. The tanks are heated, as maximum methane production during decomposition occurs over a temperature range which is higher than ambient temperature. The gas produced is collected and usually stored in a small gas holder, any excess gas being automatically burnt off. As at the Cambridge sewage works, the gas is usually used for powering dual-fuel engines coupled to alternators which provide electricity for the works itself. In Cambridge, the cooling water from the engines is circulated via a heat exchanger to heating coils inside the digester in order to maintain the necessary temperature of 33° C. The digestion process continues for approximately 30 days, and during this time the original raw sludge is stabilized into a relatively innocuous, almost black material. This, in turn, is more easily dried artificially or on beds to form a final manure much safer than the undigested sludge. The gas evolved during the digestion process is a mixture of $25 - 35$ per cent carbon dioxide and $65 - 75$ per cent methane, although small quantities of ammonia, hydrogen sulphide, hydrogen, nitrogen and oxygen may also be produced. The calorific value of the sludge gas is approximately midway between that of town gas and that of natural gas, being about 5.8 kWh/m^3. At Mogden sewage works near London, the volume of gas produced during sludge digestion is approximately 0.03 m^3 per head of population per day.

The large-scale production of methane at the sewage works has proved both successful and economic but, as can be seen, the volume of gas produced is relatively small. The amount might possibly be increased to produce a useful methane surplus by mixing pre-ground garbage, i.e. waste organic matter, with the raw sludge. The mixture digests at approximately the same rate as the sewage sludge alone and produces a much higher gas yield, although the capacity of the sludge digestion plant would also need to be increased. However, this enlargement of the size and function of the central plant could produce a situation which was no longer economically viable. Already the transport costs of distributing the valuable digested sludge from the cities where it is produced to the agricultural land where it is needed are greater than the monetary value of the sludge as fertilizer and, consequently, digested sludge is dumped in rivers or at sea, with a loss to the soil of a natural fertilizer and a gain to the agrochemical industry.

In some places farmers are encouraged to pay a minimum cost and to transport the fertilizer for themselves once it has been dried into sludge cake. It would therefore seem that the production of possibly useful quantities of methane on a large scale by collecting sewage and garbage at a central point of treatment is hampered by the problem of the redistribution of the final treated sludge, which should be a very useful fertilizer. To overcome this problem it might be better to equip every farm with an individual methane plant. The intensification of animal husbandry into smaller areas, with more specialized units replacing the 'traditional' mixed farm of the past, has so increased the volume of farm slurries that these now present a disposal problem. The large areas of 'feedlots' in the USA where cattle are fattened before slaughtering pose a similar problem, but on a much larger scale. Bohn (1971) estimates that a feedlot producing 100,000 head of cattle a year could yield sufficient gas, if the wastes were processed anaerobically, to meet the natural gas requirements of 30,000 people, given the present rate of consumption in America. Even at the farm scale, however, although the methane could provide for all the energy requirements of the house and farm and even provide power for tractors, the volume of sludge fertilizer produced could weigh against the installation of such plants, as it would not be needed on the land all year round and therefore would still present a disposal problem. This is particularly evident in the specialized farm where the amount of arable land is no longer related to the number of livestock kept.

At the other extreme, the vision of every household fitted with its own methane digester dealing with all sewage and garbage at source and producing gas as a useful by-product is also an impossibility. At the production rate for gas from sewage sludge quoted before, a family of three might produce 0.09 m^3 of gas a day. This could be raised by a further 0.09 m^3 of gas a day by mixing the sewage with the garbage produced by a three-person family, to give an over-all equivalent of 0.9 kWh of heat a day (Smith, 1973). For three people the average cooking requirements of 1,200 kWh/year (Electricity Council Research, 1972) work out as 3.0 kWh/day, and this means that the methane produced by an average family is insufficient to meet their cooking requirements. It must also be remembered that some means of maintaining the temperature of the digester must be found, and on a large scale this is often achieved by burning a portion of the gas produced, thus reducing the volume of gas available for use.

However, with an area of garden under cultivation and a consequent increase in the production of organic wastes, and with the addition of a small farm animal (hens, pig, goat, cow) to the family, methane production sufficient to meet the energy demands for cooking becomes a possibility. At the same time the fertilizer by-product can be used directly on the garden and even stored by composting in the normal manner with other fresh vegetable wastes once digestion has been completed. It might also be possible to reduce the energy requirements for cooking by eliminating unnecessary waste of heat. Ovens could be better insulated, while at the same time an oven full of food is a more efficient user of fuel than a frying pan on a ring or a grill.

Unless large centralized methane-producing plants can become more efficient in their final distribution of sludge and hence more economic to run, the small-scale decentralized unit consisting of a family growing a proportion of their own food, keeping a few hens and practising some fuel economy in the kitchen should be able to provide itself with a source of fuel for cooking, a valuable fertilizer for the garden and a means of practising autonomy in sewage disposal.

The principle of extraction of a useful fuel gas from farm and vegetable waste and even sewage was demonstrated at an exhibition in 1871 in London. This principle was later developed both for small-scale farm methane plants and for the treatment of sewage sludge in large-scale central plants, the general operation of which has already been described. Many such plants exist in Britain although there are fewer in the USA.

During the war, the shortage of available fuel led to experiments with methane plants on farms in France and Germany. Based on this experience, a plant was even built in England on a 36-hectare farm in Gloucestershire. It was made of three separate digesters, each with a capacity of approximately 9 m^3, linked to a gas holder. The yield from each digester averaged 2.8 m^3 a day during the digestion period, which lasted about 42 days. The capital cost of £500 when the plant was constructed just after the war was high, although a large part of the money was spent on insulation for the digesters. For the operation of the plant farm wastes, such as straw, were mixed with pig manure and fermented in the digesters, and the gas produced was sufficient to light and heat the farmhouse and power a small engine to grind grain for the stock.

However, in the Western countries interest waned, although methane plants are still in use in many parts of the world today, including Algeria, South Africa, Korea, France and Hungary. In 1955 the government of India appointed a team to investigate the design of methane digesters with a view to simplifying their construction and making the plants cheaper to instal. It was hoped that small, efficient plants could then be constructed by an Indian village community or even a single farm for very little money, whereas the plants used on farms in Germany during the war were relatively expensive. Ram Bux

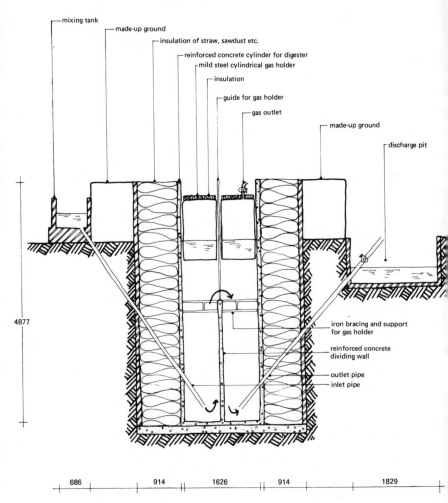

Labels on the figure:
- mixing tank
- made-up ground
- insulation of straw, sawdust etc.
- reinforced concrete cylinder for digester
- mild steel cylindrical gas holder
- insulation
- guide for gas holder
- gas outlet
- made-up ground
- discharge pit
- iron bracing and support for gas holder
- reinforced concrete dividing wall
- outlet pipe
- inlet pipe

4877

686   914   1626   914   1829

65   *Design for a double-chamber small-scale gas plant for producing about 2.8 m³ gas a day (after Singh, 1971).*

Singh (1971), the head of the Indian team, illustrates this principle by considering a seventy-million-dollar sewage works constructed at Charleston, West Virginia. He claims that scaling the plant down without altering the technology involved would mean that a plant to cater for a village or farm would still require an initial capital expenditure of half a million dollars, and only the safe processing of sewage wastes would be achieved. However, the Gobar Gas Research Station (*gobar* means cow dung in Hindi) has produced designs for plants to process wastes to a valuable fertilizer and give methane for cooking and space heating for as little as $400 (see fig. 65). Such a system of waste disposal is of particular importance in India where it is usual to collect the cow dung, dry it into cakes and then burn it as a fuel for cooking and space heating. Since the Indian farmer cannot afford to buy chemical fertilizers his crop yields are low and the land suffers as the natural manure is not returned to it. Thus, provided the capital cost was sufficiently low, a methane plant would actively improve peasant farming conditions in India by processing the dung to give fuel and fertilizer. By 1971 over 2,500 such installations had been built there.

Also under the direction of Ram Bux Singh, an experimental methane digester was constructed for *The Mother Earth News*, a magazine of alternative living, at Madison, Ohio. As in the Indian installations, the digester was a simple metal drum buried vertically in the ground with inlets and outlets for the slurry, gas and fertilizer effluent, but whereas in tropical India the ambient temperature is sufficient to maintain suitable temperatures within the digester, the design for Ohio was complicated by a water jacket encircling the digester (see fig. 66). Warm water could then be pumped through the jacket to maintain the temperature of the tank containing the fermenting wastes at $32^\circ - 35^\circ$ C. The digester was designed either to be batch fed, whereby the tank is loaded, sealed and left for 30 days to give off methane, after which time it is opened up and emptied of the digested compost, or to be operated by feeding the wastes as a slurry at regular intervals. Each addition of slurry displaces an equal volume of final compost, and in this way gas production can be continuous. Wastes could be fed daily, weekly or every fifteen days, and the experiment was designed to compare the rate at which gas was evolved with the rate at which the raw wastes were fed in. A 1.5-kW pump was installed in the system to pump ground waste material into the digester and the finished slurry from the digester, and also to circulate the digesting wastes inside. Thus it can be seen that energy must be added to the system both to maintain the correct temperature and also to operate the pump. However, the plant was designed to produce 170 m^3 of methane a month, whereas the daily twenty-minute operation of the 1.5-kW pump needed to stir the material consumed only 10 m^3 of methane a month. If the methane was used to fuel a stationary engine, the water in the jacket could be warmed with the waste heat produced, but even if it became necessary to burn some of the gas in order to maintain the temperature range inside the digester, the amount consumed should be less than that consumed by the pump.

Ram Bux Singh also suggested that the water jacket could be filled with warm waste bath water in the domestic situation. The system for *Mother Earth News* was thus designed to produce over 142 m^3 of gas a

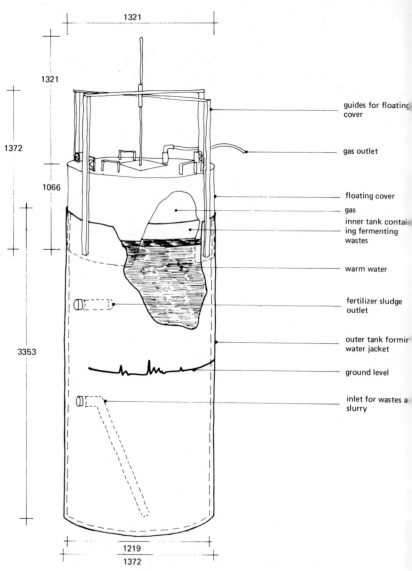

66   *Methane plant for* The Mother Earth News *(after a design by Ram Bux Singh in* Mother Earth News, *1972). The design also provided for the plant to be insulated to the top of the water jacket.*

month, plus a good quantity of valuable fertilizer. After the initial failure of the plant because the water jacket leaked, the digester is now successfully operating on a cattle farm near Redkey, Indiana, using cow manure and water as the materials for digestion.

114

For more than 18 months, the New Alchemy Institute has been operating a small digester in Santa Barbara, the design of which is based on the experience of L. John Fry and his experiments and success with methane installations in South Africa. Fry's designs (Fry and Merrill, 1973) also include a simple 'sump' digester which can be made in various sizes, with containers ranging from coffee tins to oil drums, to demonstrate that a gas really is produced when wastes decompose anaerobically. The model he constructed was made from two drums of different capacities (50 gal and 30 gal), both without tops, fitted one inside the other as shown in fig. 67. The larger drum was then filled to the height of the smaller with equal parts of waste in slurry form and a prepared 'starter' brew, which is just a liquid full of active bacteria ready to feed on the wastes. The smaller inverted drum is fitted with a small valve outlet in its base, now at the top of the whole plant, which is linked to a hose through which the gas produced can be led to storage or a burner. This type of digester can only be fed by taking off the inverted drum, removing approximately one-tenth of the digesting wastes and replacing this with fresh slurry. Depending on the size of the plant and the gas requirements, fresh material can be added daily or at regular intervals of up to three months. After each feeding operation, the small drum is pressed down to exclude any air before being left to rise up again as it fills with the gases produced.

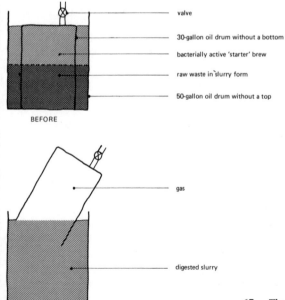

valve

30-gallon oil drum without a bottom

bacterially active 'starter' brew

raw waste in slurry form

50-gallon oil drum without a top

BEFORE

gas

digested slurry

AFTER

67   The sump digester
(after Fry and Merrill, 1973).

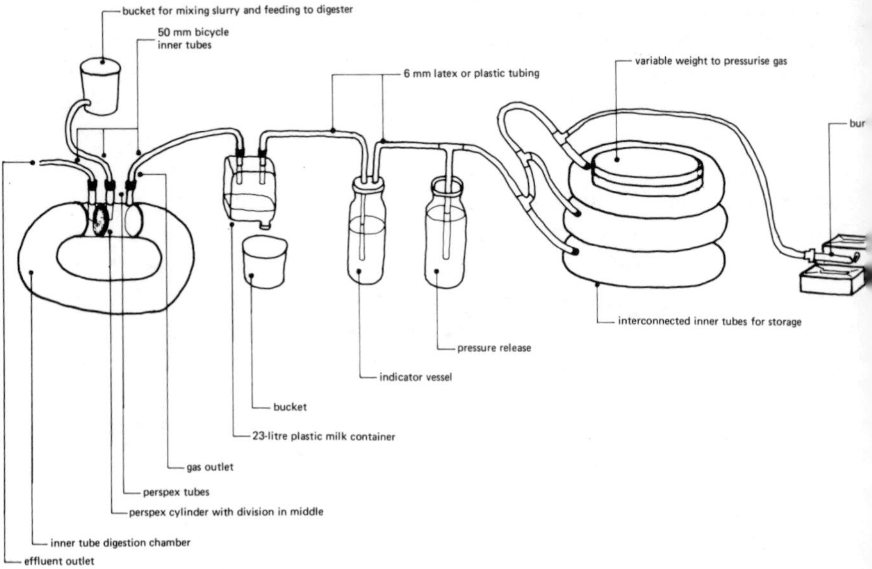

bucket for mixing slurry and feeding to digester
50 mm bicycle inner tubes
6 mm latex or plastic tubing
variable weight to pressurise gas
bur
interconnected inner tubes for storage
pressure release
indicator vessel
bucket
23-litre plastic milk container
gas outlet
perspex tubes
perspex cylinder with division in middle
inner tube digestion chamber
effluent outlet

68 Inner tube digester (after Fry and Merrill, 1973). A 23-litre milk container is suspended upside-down to trap scum coming over with the gas from the digester; this can be drawn off into the bucket by unscrewing the container cap. Gas production is shown by bubbles passing through the water in the indicator vessel. The pressure release vessel, holding 200 mm of water, keeps the gas at 200 mm water gauge pressure.

The small methane plant working in Santa Barbara cost around $20 to build, and the system is shown in fig. 68. The actual process of digestion takes place in the inner tube of a lorry or tractor tyre, and similar inner tubes are used for storing the methane. The perspex inlet and outlet pipes from the digester have been welded into a cylinder of perspex made to the same dimensions as the circumference of the inner tube, and joined to the tube to form a complete doughnut. A circular perspex panel in the middle of the cylinder separates the start of the digestion process, where the slurry inlet and methane outlet are situated, from the end, where the fertilizer effluent outlet is placed. The completed tube digester has an approximate volume of 0.1 m^3 (depending on the size of the tyre tube used), and is fed daily with 1.4 kg of chicken manure. Chicken manure is preferred as it has a finer texture and the likelihood of scum forming on the surface of the digesting wastes is therefore reduced. The chicken manure is mixed with about three litres of water or urine to a slurry in the bucket, which is then raised so that the slurry is fed by gravity into the digester. The digested slurry can be drawn off from the outlet at the other end of the digester every one or two days, the total amount removed being about half the volume of the daily input to allow for gas production and contraction during the fermentation. About 0.14 m³ of methane gas is produced daily with this system, the gas having an average calorific value of 7.3 kWh/m³, which is enough to cook a very simple meal. If the tube digester is constructed in places where the ambient temperature is too low to maintain digestion, the New Alchemy Institute recommends that the inner tube should be placed in an insulated box in which are two 100-W light bulbs connected in series and linked to a thermostat set at 35° C. The other features of the inner-tube system are shown in fig. 68.

For some years before the present increased interest in methane plants, Mr H. Bate of Totnes in Devon has been running a methane plant in conjunction with his pig and poultry holding. Part of the gas produced is compressed and used to power his 1953 Hillman car. For Bate's system, digestion is always preceded by aerobic composting for

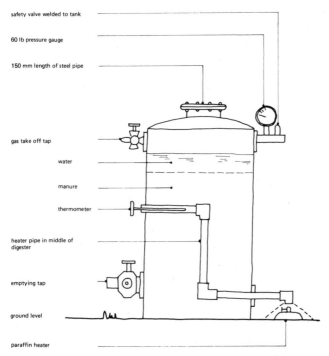

69 Conversion of 1219 mm x 610 mm domestic water heater to a methane digester (after Harold Bate). The digester is filled through the length of steel pipe welded to the top; the cover of this pipe is fixed with 9 mm bolts. The safety valve and pressure gauge, gas take-off tap, and emptying tap are also welded to the tank. The paraffin heater is replaced by a gas jet from the digester itself once digestion is under way.

approximately one week. The manure is mixed with straw and other vegetable waste, well watered and piled up into a traditional compost heap. At the end of the week, the materials are loaded into the digester and sealed from the air. Fig. 69 shows the modification of a domestic hot-water cylinder to form a methane digester. During digestion, gas production is estimated to be 0.3 m^3 for every kilogram of manure decomposed. Bate also suggests modifying a conventional septic tank into a methane digester by fitting a non-return valve to the inlet from the house, fixing a gas outlet in the vent pipe and sealing off the other vents. Gastight holes would have to be made in the lid of the tank, one to take a conventional domestic immersion heater and the other to hold a thermometer to check that the optimum temperature range of $29^{\circ} - 32^{\circ}$ C, given by Bate, is maintained. It is uncertain whether this suggestion has actually been tried, although a conventional, unaltered septic tank does process its wastes by anaerobic decomposition, the vent pipe affording a release for the gases produced, which include methane, to the air. However, if the digesting wastes are too dilute, methane formation is inhibited, and the use of a normal WC with a 9-litre flush linked to a modified septic tank would produce a water content in excess of that for optimum gas production.

Although, as discussed previously, the processing of domestic wastes in household digesters is unlikely to be possible with the small quantity of gas produced, the introduction of the modified WC equipment necessary to optimize digester conditions would also hamper the introduction of such systems. Where, however, the household is engaged in growing its own food to some extent, possibly linked with the keeping of a few hens in the backyard, so that methane production becomes worth while, it might be possible to use a WC of the type available for boats and caravans, which flushes with only 0.3 litre in the system. Alternatively, an outside WC could be built next to the digester for the members of the family who felt moved to contribute. Some other method would then have to be found to deal with the remainder of the human sewage, if it was the aim of the family to be independent of all mains services. Some devices for this purpose are already on the market, but at a high cost. They include the Clivus (see fig. 70), the Biodynamics and Microphor systems, all of which operate by some form of aerobic decomposition of the sewage. A low-cost aerobic method of treatment was worked on and tested at the Ecol house, McGill University, and with some modifications (Smith, 1973) it would be successful and cheap (see fig. 71). From this it can be seen that the methane digester is not necessarily tied in with the processing of human wastes, but could be viewed as an alternative to the compost heap. The digester could then be situated some distance from the house

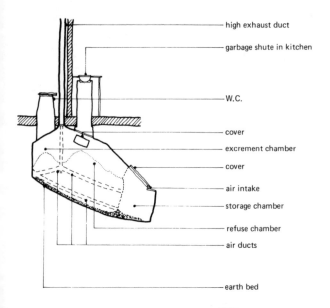

high exhaust duct

garbage shute in kitchen

W.C.

cover

excrement chamber

cover

air intake

storage chamber

refuse chamber

air ducts

earth bed

grass, leaves etc.
garden soil 50 mm
peat mould 100 mm-120 mm

70   The Clivus latrine. This is a Swedish composting unit where waste, urine etc. decompose in the presence of air. Water vapour and carbon dioxide rise up through the exhaust duct. The waste mass decreases in volume during the decomposition and drops slowly to the final storage chamber where it accumulates as compost suitable for putting on the garden, initially after 2 years in the unit and then at intervals of 1-2 years. The detail section below the diagram shows the composition of the earth bed.

(the gas being piped to the kitchen in the normal way), which might be a more comfortable situation, although the higher internal temperatures of the house would make the stabilization of the digester at optimum temperatures easier if it were built into the house. If the digester were not used to treat human sewage, the advantage of the installation would be limited to the value of the fuel and fertilizer produced by it.

A recent installation of a methane plant in Britain, at Graham Caine's Street Farmhouse in London, is interesting as algae culture is introduced into the basic decomposition cycle. The organic wastes from the house are digested aerobically and then pass into a tank which has a glass side exposed to the sun. Algae are encouraged to grow on this nutrient base in the presence of sunlight, and are then harvested and digested aerobically in exactly the same manner as vegetable wastes, to produce a small quantity of methane for cooking. The actual gain in energy terms from cultivating algae for digestion in the presence of

119

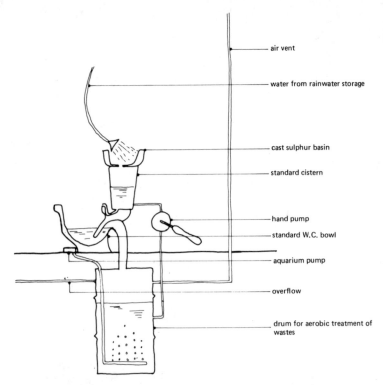

air vent

water from rainwater storage

cast sulphur basin

standard cistern

hand pump

standard W.C. bowl

aquarium pump

overflow

drum for aerobic treatment of wastes

71   *The Ecol house waste treatment system (after Ortega* et al., *1972). The W.C. is flushed with dirty water from the hand basin and the treated water from the aerobic tank which is pumped up by hand. The system operated successfully and the only smell came from the treated water standing overnight in the pumps and pipes.*

sunlight is insignificant, but exposing the algae tank to sunlight utilizes the pathogenicidal properties of the ultra-violet light. This is important, as Graham Caine intends the final effluent to feed directly to the hydroponic beds in the greenhouse adjoining the house. In the past, placing raw or dried human sewage on growing land has become associated with the spread of faecal-born diseases. To guard against such risks, systems of proper composting were developed for the third world, mainly for rural communities where outbreaks of these diseases were rife. Compost heaps made of human and animal manure layered with vegetable wastes were left for at least eight weeks to develop a temperature sufficiently high to kill the pathogenic organisms. The piles were then turned and the process repeated until the compost was safe to return to the soil, a year being the average time for such an operation. Ram Bux Singh (1971) states that where human sewage is processed anaerobically in a methane plant, the pathogens are effectively killed by lack of oxygen. However, if the final slurry were to be composted aerobically to ensure a sufficient heat for the death of any remaining pathogens, a safeguard would be provided. Further investigation is needed in this area to ascertain exactly what precautions are necessary.

Some mention of optimum temperature range, length of digestion period, types of waste and amount of gas produced has already been made, but the following section will discuss the quantities and conditions involved in more detail.

The importance of temperature in the process of anaerobic digestion has already been established. Anaerobic digestion of waste material will occur at temperatures ranging from 0° C to 69° C although bacterial action is much reduced below 16° C. Gas production is usually associated with two groups of bacteria which are differentiated by the temperature ranges over which they are active. The mesophilic bacteria are active between 29° C and 41° C and the thermophilic between 49° C and 60° C, although the latter group is more sensitive to any fluctuations in temperature. A range of 32° C $- 35^o$ C is thus usually given as the optimum for stable methane production. The actual decomposition takes place in two stages. The complex organic molecules of the waste matter are first broken down into volatile acids including acetic acid (vinegar). Only when these products have accumulated in sufficient quantity does further breakdown occur, through a second group of micro-organisms, into methane, carbon dioxide and traces of other gases. It is this second group of bacteria that is sensitive to temperature changes.

The pH range associated with decomposition and gas generation is also important and is generally accepted to be between 6.8 and 8.0, that is, slightly alkaline. However, the lower end of the range of 7.0 − 7.5 is usually found in anaerobic decomposition of sewage sludge, whereas the NAI, from experience, suggests that digesting manure and plants should, once the process has been established, be more alkaline, with a pH ranging from 8.0 to 8.5. If excess raw waste material is introduced, conditions can become too acidic, as the volatile acids are being produced faster than the methane-generating bacteria can break them down. Decomposition will then stop until more bacteria grow and the balance is restored, the time necessary for this being at least a month. Harold Bate introduced his aerobic pre-composting of wastes in order to prevent the formation of butyric acid which is believed to hamper the growth of methane-producing bacteria. It is also possible to add lime or ammonium phosphate to the contents of a digester when these have become too acidic, in order to restore the correct pH value, although alkaline sodium salts should not be added as the methane-generating bacteria die in the presence of sodium ions. Generally, the best method of preventing acid conditions is to seed the new batch of waste materials with a portion of already digested fertilizer, rich with the necessary bacteria. If digestion has started and then ceased because of acid conditions, the recirculation of some of the final effluent back into the raw wastes may also restore the balance by introducing the necessary bacteria. The need for the correction of the pH value by adding acid is very rare and if by any chance the initial material is too alkaline, the pH is soon lowered by the carbon dioxide produced during decomposition. Horse and cow manures, which are naturally more alkaline, undergo digestion more easily if they are composted aerobically first. Acids are produced during this decomposition which thus lower the pH of the manure.

Small-scale plants can be sized according to the demand for gas and the amount of digestible material available. Singh (1971) estimates that dry vegetable waste such as straw, when digested, produces approximately 0.4 m^3 of gas for every kilogram fed into the plant. Since green waste is $66 - 75$ per cent water and only the dry weight contributes to the amount of gas produced, 1 kg of green waste should yield approximately 0.2 m^3 of gas. From Rosenburg (1951) the amount of manure produced by various farm animals is registered in livestock units (see table 6). A livestock unit will produce $0.6 - 3.0 \text{ m}^3$ of gas a day depending on how the animals are confined. Even with the wide limits suggested above, it is still difficult to assess accurately the amount of gas likely to be produced even when optimum conditions are maintained within the digester, as factors such as the type of food fed to livestock will affect the manure and hence the methane potential. Any urine included with chopped-up bedding will increase gas production and, as mentioned above, conditions of confinement are important. If hens are allowed free range and only shut in to roost, the weight of the droppings collected amounts to $0.05 - 0.09$ kg a day per bird, compared with the 0.2 kg a day for a hen confined to a cage. It is also difficult to predict the amount of gas that different plants will produce as differing amounts of carbon are contained within the plant structure as lignin, which is indigestible and hence cannot be used in the formation of methane or carbon dioxide.

There is also some disagreement as to the quality of the gas produced from plant wastes. Singh (1971) states that 'pound for pound, vegetable waste results in the production of seven times more gas than animal

Table 6   Amount of manure produced by various farm animals

Type of animal	Livestock unit
Horse – heavy	1.3 – 1.5
medium	1
light	0.5 – 0.7
Bull	1.3 – 1.5
Cow and in-calf heifer	1
Young stock under 2 years	0.5
Calf under 3 months	0.1
Boar, sow	0.25
Fat pig over 70 kg	0.25
Fat pig under 70 kg	0.1
Weaner	0.02
Ewe, ram, sheep	0.1
Lamb	0.05
Goose, turkey	0.02
Duck	0.01
Hen	0.004
Man	0.02

(Taken from Miller, T. (1949) Agricultural Buildings)

waste'. However, the NAI found from their Santa Barbara experience that plant fluids from succulents such as cacti increased the proportion of gas produced by a factor that was somewhat less than seven. At the same time, laboratory experiments reported by Klein (1972) and Laura and Idnai (1971) showed that the gas produced from digesting plant wastes contained a higher percentage of carbon dioxide and correspondingly less of the useful methane. Tables 7, 8 and 9 show estimated gas production from a variety of sources.

The importance of the quantities of available carbon and nitrogen in the material for digestion has already been mentioned. This is because the bacteria involved in the anaerobic process of decomposition make use of carbon about 30 – 35 times faster than nitrogen. If the carbon: nitrogen ratio (written C/N) is higher than 30:1 in the wastes to be digested, the nitrogen is exhausted before the carbon, and a proportion of the bacteria die. As they die, the nitrogen in their cells is released and the higher ratio is thus re-established. Since fermentation ceases once all the available carbon has been consumed, any excess nitrogen remains undigested in the slurry and is lost to the air when the fertilizer is spread on the soil. Table 10 show the C/N ratios of materials which might be used for digestion; knowing the types and amounts of waste materials to be used, the final C/N ratio of the digester contents can be computed (see example, p. 134). This final ratio should fall within

123

Table 7 Gas production figures taken from working digesters

Type of manure	Gas production in m³/kg of dry matter
Pig	0.39 − 0.54
Cow (Indian)	0.21 − 0.31
Chicken	0.39 − 0.88
Conventional sewage	0.39 − 0.60

(Taken from Fry and Merrill, 1973)

Table 8 Gas production in m³/kg on a dry basis

Type of manure	m³/kg
Dung ⎱ (Singh)	0.24
Vegetable ⎰	0.45 − 0.94
Sewage sludge (Cambridge City)	0.33

(Taken from Smith, 1973)

Table 9 Gas produced from dry vegetable materials

Materials	m³/kg dry basis	Composition of gas (%)		
		methane	hydrogen	CO_2
Dry leaf powder	0.45	44	11	45
Sugarcane thresh	0.75	45	10	44
Maize straw	0.81	46	10	44
Straw powder	0.94	46	10	44
(Activated sludge	0.62	44	12	46)

(Taken from Singh, 1971)

the satisfactory limits of 30:1 to 35:1. However, experience in India has shown that cow manure, with a laboratory C/N of 25:1, is the ideal waste for immediate digestion and gas production. This illustrates the premise that the C/N ratios measured in the laboratory may differ significantly from the actual amounts of carbon and nitrogen available to the bacteria as food.

Thus it can be seen that accurate figures for the production of methane from a specific quantity and type of waste are unobtainable without an increase in the knowledge of the process of digestion. However, the following is stated as a rule of thumb, agreed on independently by Gotaas (1956) and Fry (1973): 'with good temperature

Table 10 C/N of materials for digestion

Material	Nitrogen (% dry weight)	C/N
Urine	15 – 18	0.8
Blood	10 – 14	3.0
Bone meal		3.5
Night soil	5.5 – 6.5	6 – 10
Chicken	6.3	15
Sheep	3.8	
Pig	3.8	
Horse	2.3	25*
Cow	1.7	25 or 18*
Activated sludge	5	6
Fresh sewage		11*
Grass clippings	4	12
Cabbage	3.6	12
Tomato	3.3	12.8
Mixed grasses	2.4	19
Hay, young grass	4	12
Hay, alfalfa	2.8	17*
Hay, blue grass	2.5	19
Seaweed	1.9	19
Non-legume vegetables	2.5 – 4	11 – 19
Red clover	1.8	27
Bread	2.1	
Mustard	1.5	26
Potato tops	1.5	25
Wheat straw	0.5	150
Oat straw	1.1	48
Sawdust	0.1	200 – 500

* non-lignin carbon dry weight

(Taken from Singh, 1971, and Fry and Merrill, 1973)

and raw materials, 50 – 70 per cent of the raw materials fed into the digester will be converted to bio-gas (methane).' Using such approximate values as are available, the design and sizing of a digester from a known quantity of wastes is run through at the end of this chapter (p. 134).

The processing and digestion of the raw materials can take place in two ways. For batch digestion, the wastes are loaded into a suitable pit or tank, sealed, and left to digest for one month or more, depending on the temperature and size of the plant. The gas is evolved during this period and at the end of the time, when all the gas has been given off, the digester is opened and the final fertilizer emptied out before reloading and repeating the process. In order to give a more uniform gas supply it is usual to have two or three digesters operating on the batch system but running out of phase. With three digesters, one can be left open and loaded with the raw wastes as they collect. Alternatively, the wastes can be collected and composted aerobically before loading into the emptied tank, and this ensures that a suitable temperature has built up in the raw material. Any fresh batches of waste should always be left for three days before sealing the digester, to allow aerobic composting to raise the temperature. The aerobic pre-fermentation can also help to prevent acid conditions developing within the digester, for if the contents are acidic it may be months before their pH slowly rises and conditions for full methane production are established. To overcome this, Fry (1973) suggests starting any completely new digestion process with a cultured starter brew. This is made by quarter-filling a gallon jar with active supernatant run-off from the local sewage works, or the run-off from an intensive livestock unit. Fresh manure is then added to half-fill the jar, leaving enough room for weekly additions of more fresh manure. The jar is left with the cap resting on the top but not screwed down, and the contents are shaken at intervals to stop scum forming. After some weeks the jar should be full of bacteria in the liquid, and this can be used to start digestion easily when added to a digester of raw wastes. Once the first batch of wastes has been successfully digested, further batch production proceeds easily, as the raw wastes can be seeded with some of the final bacteria-rich slurry from the working digester.

Before emptying a batch digester, the gas line must be shut off and any gas remaining left to vent to the air. The cover can then safely be removed and the fertilizer sludge forked out. Ensuring that any remaining methane is fully diluted with air is most important, as mixtures of 4 – 14 per cent of methane in air are explosive when ignited. For the same reason, the first time the gas holder or gas storage is filled after digestion starts, the gas should be expelled and the holder left to fill again, lest any air should be mixed with the gas. Although the first discharge of gas will probably not light because of the high concentration of carbon dioxide that it contains, no attempt should ever be made to light the first discharge because of the dangers of air mixed with the methane.

The batch system is most useful where the raw material is either only available at intervals or composed mostly of plant wastes: any undigested portion of the plants can then be removed when the digester is emptied. An added advantage is that batch digesters only need attention at intervals, although all moving of wastes and fertilizer sludge must be by hand.

Most of the early digester plants were of the batch type, often with several digesters operating in sequence. More recently, however, and especially in India, digesters which are loaded continuously have been designed and tested. Small quantities of waste, usually manure made up into a slurry with a consistency similar to that of cream, are added to the digester every day or almost every day. Any addition of new raw material is usually arranged to displace an equal amount of digested sludge, and in this way the gas production is maintained at a stable rate. Continuous digestion is not very suitable for plant wastes as the indigestible parts collect on the surface of the slurry within the digester as scum and, unless this can be removed, the layer builds up until digestion becomes impaired and gas production ceases. Any continous-feed digester will eventually need to be closed down and washed out so that all the scum and undigested material can be removed. Because of the build-up of scum, digesters are usually fitted with some means of agitating the liquids inside, although for small digesters the daily action of pumping in the slurry should usually be sufficient to agitate the scum. Otherwise, agitation should take place for 15 − 20 minutes each day. Although periodic agitation is useful in breaking up the surface, it has been found that continuous agitation is detrimental to methane production. It might be possible to grind up plant wastes in a compost grinder and use them in a continuous-feed system, but generally this system works best if limited to manure wastes mixed with chopped-up bedding, with the possible addition of human sewage where the amount of water that must be added with it can be controlled.

Continuous-feed digesters can be of several types, either vertical with one or two chambers, as are often used in India, or horizontal, as used at the new Santa Barbara installation (see fig. 72). The actual size of either type of continuous digester or of the batch digester is determined by the loading rate and the detention time. The detention time in turn depends on the type of material used, the temperature of the digesting contents and the rate of gas production. Table 11 relates temperature, gas production and detention time, assuming that 1 T of

Table 11   Gas production related to temperature and digestion time

Temperature (° C)	Gas production (m³/day)	Digestion period (months)
15	0.15	12
20	0.30	6
25	0.60	3
30	1.00	2
35	2.00	1

(Taken from Gotaas, 1956)

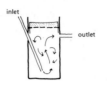

Single stage continuous flow vertical digester. As the waste digests it becomes lighter than raw wastes and rises to be displaced through the outlet. However the force with which raw wastes enter the tank may carry them past the area of maximum bacterial activity and they may emerge only partially digested.

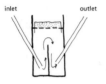

Two chamber continuous flow vertical digester. If digester is worked on a 60 day cycle digesting wastes become progressively lighter during first 30 days and rise up in first chamber. During second 30 days they become heavier and therefore the outlet is placed at the bottom of the second chamber.

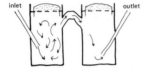

The two chamber principle extended to a larger plant. The operation is exactly the same as for the smaller plant above with approximately 80% of the total methane production coming from the first chamber and 20% from the second.

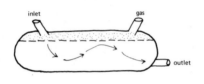

Horizontal displacement digester. The wastes progress slowly along cylinder all passing area of maximum bacterial activity to emerge fully digested at end. As scum forms evenly on surface of the digesting slurry, the larger surface area of this type of continuous flow digester will mean that it takes longer for an inhibiting layer of scum to develop.

72   Types of continuous-flow digester (after Fry and Merrill, 1973, and Singh, 1971).

manure weighing about $0.5 - 1$ T/m^3 is undergoing digestion. The exect weight of manure depends on the moisture content and the degree of compaction. Table 11 also relates gas production to temperature and digestion period and is included for comparison. The sizing of a digester in accordance with the materials available and gas production required is illustrated in the example at the end of the chapter (p. 135).

In northern climates, as has been mentioned, some method of maintaining the temperature of the digester must be found. Several simple, inexpensive methods have been suggested, including building an aerobic compost heap around the tank or trapping solar energy in a greenhouse built over it, but neither method is really capable of maintaining a steady temperature. This is best achieved by piping water through coils housed within the digester. The water can be heated in a

Table 12 Gas composition

	Unscrubbed Gas (%)	Scrubbed Gas (%)	British North Sea Gas (%)
Methane	53.8 — 62	98	95
Carbon dioxide	37 — 44.7	1	2.9
Hydrogen	0.3	—	—
Carbon monoxide	0.1	—	—
Nitrogen	1.0	1.0	—
Oxygen	0.1	—	—
Hydrogen sulphide	trace	—	—
Ethane	—	—	0.5
Propane	—	—	0.2
Butane	—	—	0.1
C_5H_{12} and above	—	—	1.3

(Taken from Rosenburg, 1951 column 1 and Bell et al., 1973 cols. 2 and 3)

flat-plate solar collector or by burning a portion of the methane collected. The heat required can be reduced by insulating the tank and burying it in the ground to minimize the heat lost from the digester to its surroundings. A closed-cell insulating material must be used, as otherwise methane may mix with the air in the pores of the insulating material at concentrations within the danger limits of 4 — 14 per cent methane in air, giving a risk of explosion.

The gas generated during decomposition has a calorific value of 5.6 — 7.2 kWh/m^3 and is composed as shown in table 12. As can be seen, once the raw methane is scrubbed it is very similar in composition to natural gas. The scrubbing removes both the corrosive and the non-combustible portions of the raw gas. Water vapour can be removed by passing the gas through a desiccant such as calcium chloride, and removal at source will prevent any condensation within the gas pipe and subsequent rusting of mild steel pipes. The calcium chloride can be regenerated by heating to drive off the absorbed water. The carbon dioxide and ammonia can both be removed by passing the gas through lime water, both gases reacting with the lime water to produce calcium carbonate and ammonium carbonate. The trace of hydrogen sulphide can be removed by passing the gas through iron filings, which can later be regenerated on exposure to air. Even when effectively scrubbed, however, the methane may not burn in a common natural-gas burner, as correct burning also depends on the pressure at which the gas is supplied. Although the flame may stay on the burner at pressures below the 2.3 kilonewtons per square metre (kN/m^2) of British North Sea gas, the gas will not be burnt efficiently and less heat will be recovered.

Alternatively, a burner can be designed for the gas as it comes from the digester with the corrosive components of water vapour and hydrogen sulphide removed. Singh (1971) gives figures for unscrubbed methane gas with a calorific value of 5.8 kWh/m^3 which burns in a designed burner with 60 per cent efficiency to give an effective value of 3.5 kWh/m^3. The actual design of such a burner is discussed at the end of the chapter (p. 134). The Hutchinson Tunnel Co. Ltd., who manufacture methane plants in Kenya, make a number of appliances and conversions to run off the gas produced. These range from methane cookers and burners, gas lights, water heaters and boilers to conversions of paraffin refrigerators and stoves.

In using methane for cooking, some method of storing the gas must be found for periods when meals are not being prepared. Storage can be achieved by placing a floating cover over the digesting wastes, especially where the digester is a vertical tank in the ground, or by piping the gas to a holder which is a miniature version of the gasometers used for town gas in Britain. Both types are shown in figs. 65 and 73. Depending on the size and material used in the construction of the cover or holder counterbalance weights may be needed to reduce the weight on the gas and hence the pressure at which it is supplied. Alternatively, a very light cover may need to be weighted to give a pressure of 0.3 − 2.3 kN/m^2, which is accepted as the design pressure range. Guides are often provided where large quantities of gas are stored, to keep the cover level as it rises.

With the escalating crisis in the oil industry, much acclaim has been given in 'alternative' literature to the value of methane as a fuel for transport. Theoretically the calorific value for pure methane of 14.7 kWh/kg is higher than that of petrol (11.6 − 12.3 kWh/kg). The toxic emissions of carbon monoxide and unburned hydrocarbons are approximately halved when an internal-combustion engine is run on natural gas or methane from wastes rather than on petrol. As with propane-fuelled cars, the alterations needed on a standard engine are in the carburettor and fuel intake. Despite these seeming attractions, there are drawbacks to the use of methane as a petroleum substitute. A gas at normal temperature and pressure, methane can only be liquefied at a pressure of nearly 34,000 kN/m^2. This makes storage of the gas in a moving vehicle a problem. During the war, when both methane and wood-gas were used to power transport, it was common to see a car surmounted by a large, silvery gas-filled bag made of barrage balloon fabric. However, the most convenient way of transporting the gas is in bottles under a pressure ranging from 690 to 21,000 kN/m^2, depending on the type of compressing equipment available. Compressing the gas requires energy, however, and the over-all efficiency of the system

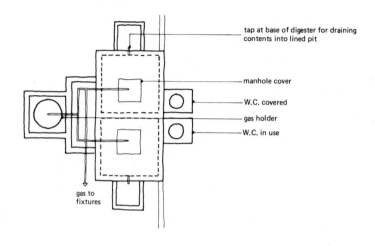

tap at base of digester for draining contents into lined pit

manhole cover

W.C. covered

gas holder

W.C. in use

gas to fixtures

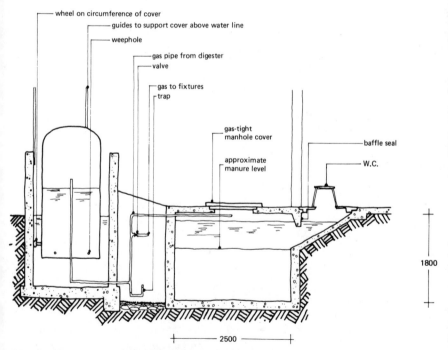

wheel on circumference of cover

guides to support cover above water line

weephole

gas pipe from digester

valve

gas to fixtures

trap

gas-tight manhole cover

approximate manure level

baffle seal

W.C.

1800

2500

73 *Design for W.C. to feed directly into one of two batch digesters linked to a separate gas holder (after designs by Gotaas, 1956). With such a system, addition of human sewage to a working digester would finish one month before the end of the digestion period, and the second W.C. would then be put into operation.*

131

immediately drops. Fry (1973) computes that running a 4.5-kW (6 h.p.) rototiller on methane with a 25 per cent compressor efficiency would require 0.4 kWh to compress an equivalent 7.4 kWh of energy contained in the gas, which itself only provides 2.0 kWh of work, the remaining energy being dissipated as heat, as the conventional gas engine is only 25 per cent efficient. This system is less efficient even than the 10 per cent conversion of petrol to energy in an internal-combustion engine. The efficiency could be raised by using the methane to power a stationary engine, either to power farm machinery or for generating electricity, and then circulating the cooling water back through coils in the digester to heat the contents.

The other big drawback to any dream of individual transport run on methane is the quantity of gas that can be produced on a small scale. It is estimated (Rosenburg, 1951) that a cow kept inside could give the equivalent of 1.8 litres of petrol a day, using a conversion where 1 litre of petrol is equivalent to 1.2 m^3 of gas. From this it can be seen that the stabled family cow could supply fuel for an average of 120 km a week. However, there would be difficulties and potential dangers in compressing the gas on a small scale, especially in ensuring that the equipment and lines were clear of air before commencing compression, and for these reasons methane-powered transport is not very attractive. The most useful application, granted that compression could be achieved satisfactorily, would be at farm level, where methane could be used for powering tractors and farm machinery. Rosenburg (1951) suggests that 8 – 20 livestock units would be required to keep a 19-kW (25 h.p.) tractor working for 1000 hours a year.

The generation of useful quantities of methane from waste materials seems in the Western world to be applicable to two, or possibly three, sizes of plant. These are the central sewage works, the family with a large garden and some livestock who could use the gas for cooking, and the mixed farm which can provide both the wastes and the land on which to spread the fertilizer sludge.

The question of the central works is interesting, as it might be possible to exploit the fuel on a larger scale if integration of waste disposal was feasible, but the large capital costs involved would probably prohibit this development without some impetus from impending fuel and resource shortages and the resultant need to practise fuel economy. In Leicester, however, foresight in the planning of the sewage works and refuse disposal gave a system where the anaerobically digested sewage sludge is partially dewatered by filtration and mixed with sorted town refuse. The whole is then composted aerobically in a slowly revolving cylinder which forcibly aerates the mixture. If the sludge (C/N 18:1) is mixed with municipal refuse (C/N approximately 70:1) and composted, the final product is a saleable agricultural compost with a C/N of 20:1 or lower, which approaches the C/N of 10:1 found naturally in well-decayed humus and cell protoplasm.

On the household scale, any production of methane requires some physical activity in loading and unloading the digester, whether it is of the batch or continuously-loaded type. However, the inner tube digester, which is the smallest plant described, produces 0.14 m^3 of gas a day from only 1.4 kg of chicken manure, which is also reckoned to be easily digestible and a good gas producer. About $15 - 30$ roosting hens would be necessary, therefore, to produce enough gas to boil 2 litres of water for 20 minutes. The fertilizer sludge is also important on the small scale as it is a valuable soil and plant food for gardens which are worked intensively to give vegetables all the year round. Recently reported experiments have even indicated that the nitrogen as it occurs in the sludge in the form of ammonium bicarbonate is more readily available to the plants than the nitrites and nitrates produced by aerobic composting. The sludge is usually allowed to stand before being applied to the soil so that any ammonia it contains, which would be harmful to plants, can escape to the air. Otherwise sludge is applied in the same way as normal garden compost, with a little care to see that it does not make the soil too acidic, or alter the soil structure (as it is wetter than ordinary compost). From all this it can be seen that the benefits of methane as a 'free' fuel for cooking require some work on the part of the beneficiary plus some capital investment in the digester and other plant. The value of the gas can be offset against this cost although, where the desire is to be independent of all mains services, the owner may be prepared to pay slightly more for his gas than the price of equivalent amounts of commercial gas in order to gain autonomy. However, cost increases in conventional fuels could soon alter this situation. If human sewage is added to the digester, the cost of the plant is reduced, since the money normally spent on sewage treatment is saved. The plant, too, can range from the relatively sophisticated prefabricated unit to parts picked up from the junk heap. However, respect should at all times be accorded to the potential hazards involved, and care is needed in all construction work to see that the joints are properly made and sealed. Nevertheless, there are many successful plants in operation all over the world, from India to the USA, which show that with some effort, working with nature can be at least as profitable as paying out money in order to benefit from a despoiled environment.

Design of digester for an autonomous house (Vale, 1973)

Availability of materials

			Total
People (3 av.) faeces		0.18 kg/head/day	0.54 kg/day
People (3 av.) urine		1.14 l/head/day	3.42 l/day
Pig	1	3.77 kg/day	3.77 kg/day
Goat	2 (if paddocked, half manure should be recoverable)	1.72 kg/head/day	1.72 kg/day

For green waste, allow for production of 5 T/ha twice a year (two crops are allowed for as gardens are cultivated intensively, e.g. early peas followed by brussels sprouts), since root vegetables produce 5 – 22.5 T/ha of leaves, i.e. waste, and wheat produces 3.75 T/ha of straw. Therefore, with 0.3 ha under cultivation of some kind, it might be possible to gain 5 x 0.3 x 2 T/year of waste = 3 T/year = 8.2 kg/day. At the same time, the addition of 0.45 kg of straw from the animal litter is allowed for, as this is rich in carbon and will help to balance the night soil and urine which are rich in nitrogen.

Since the process is one of continuous digestion, small amounts of waste as estimated above should be added daily. If this is done, a steady gas production should result, although Singh (1971) suggests that weekly addition of material would also be satisfactory. This would be advantageous for a family, even if human sewage was added daily, as the weekend scraping of dropping-boards, and gardening activities, could be combined with attending to the methane plant.

Suitability of materials

Material	Weight (kg)	Dry weight (kg)	Nitrogen (% dry weight)	C/N of material	Nitrogen content	Carbon content
Faeces	0.54	0.16	5.5 – 6.5	6 – 10	0.010	0.077
Urine	–	0.19	15 – 18	0.8	0.030	0.024
Manure	5.49	1.10	1.7	25	0.019	0.468
Green waste	8.20	2.05	2.7	17.8	0.055	0.985
Straw	0.45	0.45	0.3	128	0.001	0.179
					0.115	1.733

C/N of materials = 1.733/0.115 = 15:1

Such a ratio would probably be acceptable, although rather low.

The C/N of the materials is worked out knowing the percentage of nitrogen in the dry weight of the various substances (see any agricultural chemistry textbook) and the C/N of the green wastes is taken as an average from the values for various vegetation, e.g. cabbage, tomato, mixed grasses, grass clippings, mustard, potato haulm etc. This gives an average nitrogen content of 2.7 per cent dry weight and a C/N of 17.8. Dry weights are found as green wastes are approximately 80 per cent water by weight.

Since human sewage was to be added with the other wastes a period of 3 months would probably be necessary for the digestion, to eliminate any danger of disease. However, as the transmission of diseases in such a system has not been studied in any detail, a detention period of 2 months was selected to limit the size of the digester; the final sludge was to be mixed with dry wastes and composted aerobically for a further time to allow a sufficient temperature to build up to ensure the destruction of all pathogens. The compost would be ready to put back on the soil after 6 months to 1 year. As the C/N of 15:1 was richer in nitrogen than the recommended value of 30:1 − 35:1 this further composting will help to retain some of the excess of nitrogen which would otherwise be lost to the air as ammonia if the sludge were spread directly on the soil. To increase the C/N ratio more straw, rich in carbon, could be added. This would also increase gas production.

Gas production (using conservative values)

Material	Gas production (m^3/kg)	Total gas produced (m^3)
Human and animal manure	0.25	0.36
Green waste	0.5	1.03
Straw	0.8	0.36
		1.75 m³

Daily gas consumption for a family of four practising reasonable fuel economy in the kitchen, i.e. oven full when on, is about 1.5 m³/day.

Sizing the digester

The digester contents should be 7 − 9 per cent total solids so the added waste must be ground and mixed to a slurry with water. Since 1 kg of dry matter must be mixed with 10 kg of water to give 9 per cent solids, the following table shows the amount of water that must be added to each daily addition of material to give 9 per cent solids in the digester.

Material	Dry weight (kg)	Water content (kg)	Water to be added (litres)
Human & animal manure	1.26	4.77	7.8
Green waste	2.04	6.12	14.3
Straw	0.45	0	4.5

Liquid added as urine = 3.4 litre/day
Water added when flushing WC = 9.0 litre/day (0.5-litre flush)
Therefore water to be added with plant waste and manure
$$= 26.6 - 12.4 \text{ litre/day} = 14.2 \text{ litre/day}$$

135

Since this value gives just over 9 per cent solids the amount of water added could be slightly above this, say 15 litre/day.

Using a 50-day digestion period:

Material	Amount added in 50 days (kg)	Volume occupied (m³)
Human and animal manure	301.5	0.26
Vegetable waste and straw	432.5	0.88
Water and urine	1370.0	1.37
		2.51

Although wastes are being added and withdrawn daily, the total volume in the digester, once the system is established, will be equal to that added during the full 50-day cycle. Therefore the digester size = 2.5 m³, say 1 x 1 x 2.5 metres.

Temperature

The temperature of the digesting wastes is held at 30° C. This inside temperature is achieved by insulating the digester and raising the temperature of the contents with the waste heat contained in used bath and washing water. If the water is added at the temperature of the cistern in the attic, i.e. 15° C, then heat must be added to the digester to bring the water temperature up to the required 30° C. This assumes that the wastes added have already been digested aerobically to raise their temperature, and that human faeces and urine are added at body temperature of 37° C. The digester is then well insulated so that heat lost from the contents at a temperature of 30° C to the surrounding soil is kept to a minimum.

The system designed uses a holding tank for waste hot water from the bath, basin and kitchen sink (washing-up water only) placed under the digester (see diagram). This tank is also well insulated. The water then cools from an estimated temperature of 35° C for the water from the bathroom and 45° C for the water from dish-washing to the temperature of the digesting contents of 30° C. This heat gain to the digester must be sufficient to raise the temperature of the water added to 30° C and also to balance the heat loss of the whole digester and tank unit to the soil. Thus:

heat evolved by water in cooling = heat loss from digester + heat gain to water

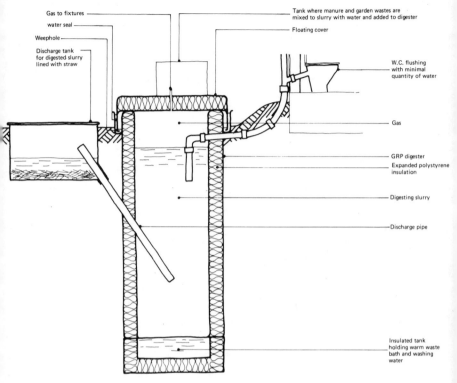

74 Possible form for methane digester as calculated.

Knowing the quantities of both the hot and cold water added and the temperatures involved it is possible to calculate the amount of insulation needed to maintain the digester temperature. However, this problem is really more complicated than the following simplified calculation. The problem is really a dynamic one as the addition of 45° C or 30° C water to the tank under the digester will increase the heat loss from the tank. To give an approximate value for the insulation thickness the digester and tank are assumed to be at a steady-state temperature of 30° C:

Heat needed to raise the temperature of water from 15° C to 30° C

$$= (15 + 9) \times (30 - 15) \times 1 \text{ kcals}$$

$$= 360 \text{ kcals.}$$

This amount of heat is needed every 24 hours, therefore rate of heating

137

= 360/24 kcals/hour = 17.4 watts

Similarly, heat evolved as water cools

= 45 x (45 − 30) x 1 + 195 x (35 − 30) x 1 kcals

= 1650 kcals.

Rate of heat evolved

= 1650/24 kcals/hour = 80.0 watts

Assume the average soil temperature is 2° C. If the digester is 1 m^2 in area and 2.5 m high and the waste-water tank underneath is 1 m^2 in area and 0.24 m high, the total surface area of the unit is 13 m^2 including the top and base. However, to find the heat loss through the insulated digester the external area of the insulated digester should be taken. Assuming that the insulation is 100 mm thick, the surface area of the digester becomes 16 m^2. If U W/m^2 deg C is the U-value of the insulated digester, then

U x 16 x (30 − 2) = 80.0 − 17.4

From which U = 0.14 W/m^2 $^\circ$C

Since the conductivity of expanded polystyrene is 0.033 W/m $^\circ$C

Thickness of polystyrene = 0.033/0.14 m = 0.23 m, or approximately 200 mm.

Using this method for heating the digester the exact amount of insulation is difficult to determine as the temperature of the waste water may vary from day to day. More important, the temperature of the soil will vary (see Chapter 4) and in summer very little additional heat will be needed as the heat loss from the well-insulated digester will be much smaller with soil temperatures of $15^\circ − 20^\circ$ C between 0.5 and 1 m below ground, than with the temperature of 2° C used in the calculations. It might be that only the heat from waste bath and basin water would be needed in the summer to maintain the temperature of the digesting wastes within the $30^\circ − 35^\circ$ C temperature range. This calculation has only been included to show a rough approximation for the amount of insulation that might be needed to maintain digester temperature in a British winter.

6 The problem of water

Even in rural areas where mains drainage and gas cannot be economically supplied, a tap giving fresh, pure water is accepted as standard in Britain. The water resources in Britain should theoretically be adequate to meet any future increase in demand (Department of the Environment, 1972). The Scottish resources are considered more than adequate and in England and Wales, where the present over-all consumption is equivalent to a run-off of 50 mm, a further 150 mm out of the total of 500 mm average run-off per year could be exploited. North America also receives enough water to meet all its needs (Committee on Resources and Man, 1969).

In both countries, the problem lies in trying to supply all the country with water, and not just the areas where it is plentiful. The planning of new reservoirs in hitherto unspoiled countryside brings outcries from the environmentalists, but without new areas of water storage the drier areas of the country risk being without a water supply for at least some part of the year. The obvious site for new reservoirs is close to metropolitan areas, but this would take large amounts of land needed for supplying food for the same cities. New York has already been forced to draw water from 225 kilometres away, and Los Angeles pumps water from sources 320 kilometres north and 400 kilometres east of the city. At the same time, the water supply must be shared between industrial, agricultural and domestic demands. Industry could be offered an incentive to recycle by increasing the price paid to the authority — for example, the 37 tonnes of water at present used to make 1 tonne of steel could be reduced, by recycling the water, to 4 tonnes of water per tonne of steel (Department of the Environment, 1972) — but any attempt to reduce domestic consumption by metering would involve such high capital and administrative costs as to be impractical.

Accepting the fact that any rainwater falling on a man-made environment is already piped through surface-water or foul sewers to the treatment works before passing into a watercourse with the final purified effluent, it might be possible for each person to use the water that falls naturally on his piece of the environment, without waiting for it to seep into the ground or run through sewers to the watercourse, only to be withdrawn again into reservoirs, stored, purified and piped back to his tap.

Table 13 (Smith, 1973) shows a comparison, taken from various sources, of the average amount of water consumed per person per day. The breakdown indicates the areas where immediate savings could be made if alternative methods of water supply and sewage disposal were to be adopted. The wasted water, which forms approximately 13 per cent of the total supply to the consumer, is lost through leaks and bursts in underground supply pipes, and this is eliminated as soon as water collection, purification and treatment are performed at the household scale. By far the highest water consumer in both Britain and the USA is the W.C., which flushes a third of the water supply back into the sewers. The amount of water used is higher in the USA than in Britain as the standard cistern is larger.

Table 13 Average per capita water usage in litre/head/day

Item	UK average (Sharp, 1967)	all (March, 1971)	hot	cold	US average (Fair, 1966)	small flats (Webster, 1972)	large flats
W.C.	50	43		43	78		
Personal hygiene	45	55	40	15	70		
Laundry	15	21	7	14	8	cold at kitchen sink 17	22
Dishes	15	6	5	1	17		
Drinking & cooking	5	4		4	10	cold elsewhere 68	62
Garden & car	10	2		2	7	hot water 50	53
Losses	20				30*		
TOTAL	160	131	52	79	220	135	137

* Domestic water consumption is 1/3 of total (domestic 190 litre/head/day, commercial and industrial 250 litre/head/day, public 40 litre/head/day, unaccounted 90 litre/head/day; total 570 litre/head/day) therefore 1/3 of unaccounted is allocated to domestic.

Apart from the introduction of expensive new lavatories designed for caravans which flush with a quarter of a litre of water or with recycled effluent, an immediate reduction in the amount of clean water supplied could be achieved with a little alteration in the plumbing system which would probably not cost a great deal. Dirty water from baths, washbasins and possibly laundry could easily be collected up, especially

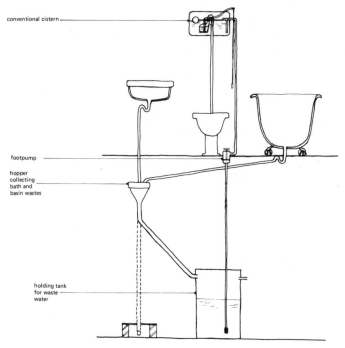

conventional cistern

footpump

hopper
collecting
bath and
basin wastes

holding tank
for waste
water

75   *A system which could easily be applied to existing housing stock, whereby the W.C. is flushed with waste soapy water.*

where they flow through a hopper, and used to flush the conventional W.C. (see fig. 75). In both Britain and the USA, the average laundry and personal hygiene requirements match or slightly exceed the volume of water needed for flushing the lavatory, and since the water eventually returns to the same sewers, the system would not really be affected. Alternatively, if some other method of dealing with human sewage, using little or no water, has been provided in the house, independently of the mains sewers, then the total demand is considerably reduced. Other water-saving equipment could also be introduced, such as showers to replace baths, and atomized sprays instead of running water for hand-washing. At the same time, the quality of the water supplied through the tap has to be very high to make it suitable for drinking, whereas the actual demand for drinking and cooking water is only 3 per cent of the present total consumption. This is important as, if each autonomous household is to have some way of purifying water for drinking, the equipment and cost could be reduced if this volume of water could be kept low. If rainwater is the source there is no real reason why this should not be used directly, after screening, for

141

washing and similar purposes. Wallman (1972) dismisses home treatment and recycling of wastes as being too costly and, in the hands of unqualified home-owners, a potential hazard to health: 'even if potable water were excluded from the recycle system, a potential health hazard would still exist because water from other outlets, such as bath or shower, is frequently swallowed by children.' But Smith (1973) considers this too reactionary, as the dangers to the health of children already exist, if misused, in present homes in the form of the open W.C. bowl, dustbin or bath.

Depending on the amounts of water that can be collected by each household, the scale for cleaning and recycling water can be established. Space flight has demonstrated that it is possible, at a very high cost, to recycle all drinking water and food through the body and purify and monitor it so that it is free of all contaminants and pathogens and can be drunk again. Such total recycling would probably never be needed for the house, as there is always some rainwater which can be purified for drinking, while the sewage can be dealt with independently from any waste-water treatment.

The sources from which domestic water can be collected are quite numerous and can be classified into three types: underground water, including springs, wells and boreholes; surface water, including streams and rivers; and rainwater collected directly from roofs. The exploitation of the first two categories will depend on where the house is located, but the third system of rainwater collection and purification should be possible in any temperate climate. In fact, the rainfall of any country is the original source of all water supplies, as it has been estimated that when rain falls approximately one-third evaporates soon after falling, one-third runs off by surface drainage to increase the volume of lakes, rivers and streams, and the remainder sinks into the ground to feed underground supplies such as wells and springs or is absorbed by plants and trees. The rain that falls during the autumn, winter and spring will form the basis of any household system, as in summer a larger proportion of the rainfall evaporates, and because of this any method of collection must be linked to some form of storage.

Rainwater is the purest of the three sources listed, although it will have absorbed many impurities during its passage through the atmosphere and these impurities will vary according to the location. The high concentration of lead in the London atmosphere is absorbed by the rainwater and becomes very difficult and expensive to remove. In most rural areas, however, the rainwater is very soft and insipid to the taste, and is easily contaminated. Roofs that are going to be used as rainwater catchment areas should therefore be constructed of satisfactory materials and maintained in good order so that contamination is reduced. The best materials are corrugated galvanized steel, corrugated asbestos cement, or glass, and the roof should be given as steep a slope as possible. The gutters and downpipes should be protected against corrosion, and lead should not be used for any part of the system. Formerly, lead was most commonly used on roofs for the flashings round chimneys, but because of the high price of lead these flashings are now usually made of super-purity aluminium. Lead should not be used, as it will dissolve in soft water and lead salts are cumulatively poisonous. To reduce evaporation losses, the collected water should be piped directly to covered storage tanks for further treatment.

If no recycling of water were to be carried out, apart from using waste washing water for flushing a conventional W.C. cistern, the average amount of water to be collected and stored in Britain would be 80 litres a head per day, ignoring any water needed for the garden and assuming that waste laundry water could be used to clean the car. Using the method outlined in the *Village Technology Handbook* (1970), the area of roof needed to supply this amount of water can be calculated as follows:

For 3-person family, total daily requirement = 240 litres
Yearly average rainfall (e.g., for Cambridge) = 549 mm
Minimum rainfall expected, taking 2/3 of average = 366 mm
(A rainfall of 1 mm/m^2 is equivalent to 1 $litre/m^2$)
Total yearly requirement = 240 x 365 litres
Therefore area of collection = 240 x 365/366 m^2
$$= 239 \ m^2$$

The Village Technology Handbook suggests adding 10 per cent of this value to allow for water lost by evaporation and by discarding the initial run-off at the beginning of each rainfall. Therefore,

total area = 239 + 24 m^2 = 263 m^2

As can be seen, this total is much larger than the area of the average roof, which measures about 50 m^2. There might be some possibility of increasing this collection area by collecting rainfall from greenhouses, although the usual practice of collecting this rainwater in a water-butt and using it for the plants inside cannot then be carried out. In the same way, if animals are kept in a decentralized autonomous situation, their water requirements must also be met. A goat in milk will consume 22 – 27 litres of water a day, and this alone will require a collection area of around 26 m^2 for each goat, without any allowance made for water for cleaning out. Thus it appears that in the east and south-east of England,

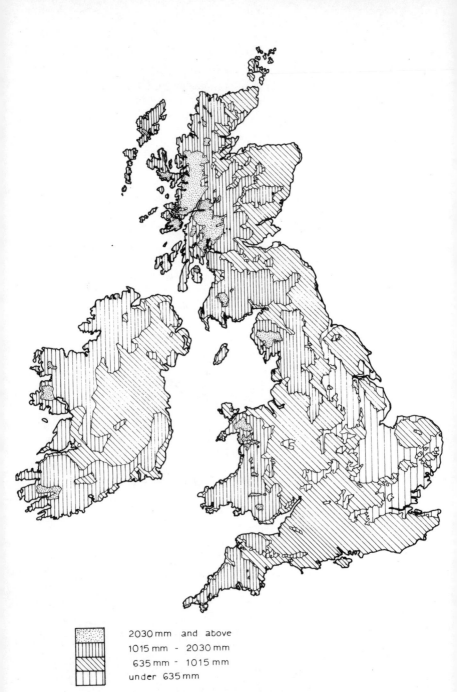

2030 mm and above
1015 mm - 2030 mm
635 mm - 1015 mm
under 635 mm

76   *Average annual rainfall for British Isles.*

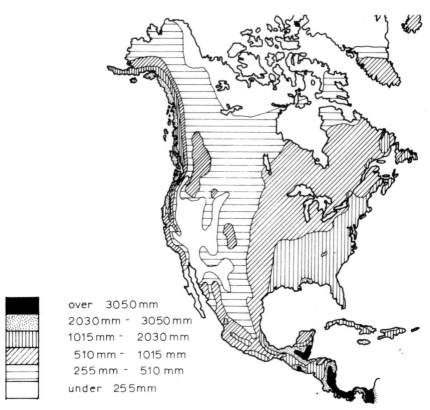

over 3050 mm
2030 mm – 3050 mm
1015 mm – 2030 mm
510 mm – 1015 mm
255 mm – 510 mm
under 255 mm

77   *Average annual rainfall for North America.*

where the average rainfall of 500 – 660 mm is the lowest in Britain,
more purification and recycling of waste water would be necessary,
together with the elimination of the conventional W.C. using too much
water, in order to balance collection and requirements. Since any
animal housing will have a roof area insufficient for the drinking water
requirements of the animals, their needs must also be considered where
they are included in the over-all design of an autonomous system.
Assuming that only the water for drinking and for dish-washing, which
is greasy, are lost for ever from the system, then the three-person
family would require only 60 litres a day, which might just be provided
by a roof of conventional size plus a shed or greenhouse. However, in
the remainder of Britain the situation would not be so critical. The
average annual rainfall for the north and west is approximately 1,525 mm,
the average for all England being 840 mm and for the whole of the
British Isles 1,205 mm. The maps show isohyets for both Britain and
the USA.

145

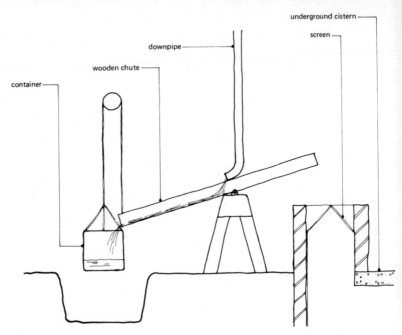

78　*A device for separating off the first flow of rainwater from a roof.*
A wooden chute is pivoted off-centre on a supporting framework and so remains
at rest as shown. The first rainwater from the roof runs down the chute and fills
the suspended container. When the weight of water in the container is greater
than the extra weight in the long arm of the chute the equilibrium is broken, the
container falls and the chute is tipped as shown below.

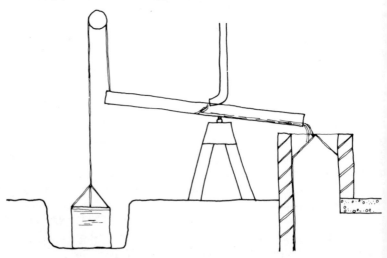

The rain-water now flows down the shorter arm of the chute, over a screen, to an
underground cistern. After the rain the container must be emptied and the
original equilibrium restored. The container must be of a size to hold sufficient
water for washing the roof.

146

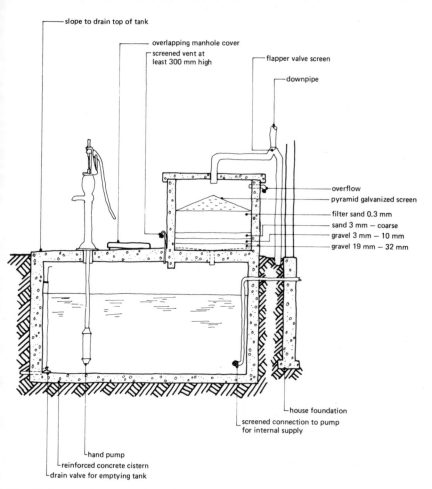

slope to drain top of tank

overlapping manhole cover

screened vent at least 300 mm high

flapper valve screen

downpipe

overflow

pyramid galvanized screen

filter sand 0.3 mm

sand 3 mm — coarse

gravel 3 mm — 10 mm

gravel 19 mm — 32 mm

house foundation

screened connection to pump for internal supply

hand pump

reinforced concrete cistern

drain valve for emptying tank

79   *Underground concrete cistern for rainwater with integral slow sand filter (after US Public Health Service, Joint Committee on rural sanitation, 1950).*

Once collected, the water is piped to some form of covered storage. It is usual to allow the first portion of rain to run off the roof to wash away dirt and bird droppings. Fig. 78 shows a device for separating out this first flow from the water to be collected. The size of the rainwater storage tank depends on the daily requirements and the length of time between rainfall. In Britain, it is usually large enough to accommodate at least a quarter of the estimated annual yield. The storage cistern can be a series of prefabricated metal tanks, or it may be made of any suitable material, such as bricks, concrete or butyl rubber. The tanks, which are usually situated above ground, are easy to install and keep clean, but making a brick-lined or concrete cistern in the ground has the advantage of keeping the stored water cool and sweet before it is purified. Fig. 79 shows a classic concrete cistern designed for developing countries (Wagner and Lanoix, 1959), which incorporates a sand filter above the underground storage tank. The concrete walls and floor of the tank are best poured at the same time, using a cement-rich mix, and the surface is kept damp for the following ten days to prevent the formation of cracks as the concrete dries. The floor of the cistern is sloped so the water can be more easily siphoned or bailed out for cleaning. An overflow pipe is not included, adjustments to the flow of water being made by means of the valve at the bottom of the downpipe, but a vent covered with a copper screen to prevent insects entering the tank must be provided to allow the air displaced by the water to leave the cistern. The cistern can be fitted with a hand pump, or connected to a power pump and a tank inside the house. A small pipe with a screw cap in the top of the cistern allows for measuring the contents with a dipstick, and also for chlorinating the water inside the tank after every fresh fall of rain. The sand filter removes most of the organic matter from the rainwater, but chlorination is used here as the means of achieving bacterial purity so that the water is fit for drinking. After the rain, the amount of water is measured and a 5 ppm (parts per million) dose of chlorine is administered. The mechanics of home chlorination are discussed later, together with other means of purifying water for drinking. It is also necessary to wash the cistern out with a 50 ppm solution of chlorine when it is first built, and then rinse it well with clean water.

The complications introduced in the above rainwater-storage system come from the fact that the water is purified before storing. Other storage systems depend on storing the collected water for purification later. The butyl-rubber-lined hole for water storage (see fig. 80) is very simple and cheap to construct and works on this principle. A very simple way of constructing a concrete rainwater tank, originally designed for water for the garden, is shown in fig. 81. The hole is prepared, and cardboard boxes of earth are used as a formwork for the concrete; alternatively, such a tank could be made by lining a hole with plastered brick. Where the water is not stored in a purified condition, underground storage is probably the best method. Rainwater collected and stored in this way has in the past been recognized as the best for laundry and hair-washing as it is very soft and consequently takes less soap to lather well.

Whether water is taken from surface or underground sources, as is usual on the large scale, or whether the relatively pure rainwater is collected, some method must be found of purifying it so that it is fit to

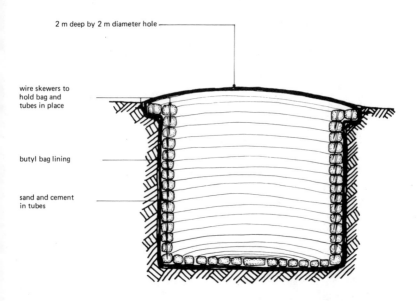

2 m deep by 2 m diameter hole

wire skewers to
hold bag and
tubes in place

butyl bag lining

sand and cement
in tubes

*80   Underground butyl rubber rainwater cistern to store 4,546 litres (after
Butyl Products Ltd, Billericay, England). The cistern is covered with a butyl
sheet pegged to the ground. The inner lining consists of perforated plastic
tubes, filled with sand and cement, soaked in water and used wet. (Below)
Diagram to show forms for the 41 m² collecting basin. The basin is formed of
earth beaten to give a smooth and impervious surface, the outer edges of the basin
being 200 mm higher than the top of the tank.*

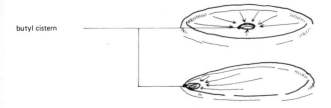

butyl cistern

drink and cook with. The most usual method of treatment proceeds in
three stages: primary screening and sedimentation, secondary filtration,
and some type of sterilization or tertiary treatment. Flash distillation
treatments, specifically for saline and brackish waters which contain
too high a proportion of dissolved solids to be treated in the normal
way, have also been developed on a large scale to increase the supply of
pure water, but water produced in this way is usually more expensive
as the flash distillation process requires electricity. However, both

149

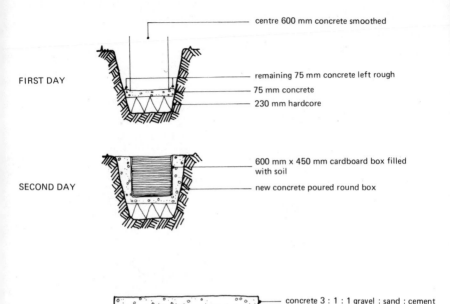

FIRST DAY — centre 600 mm concrete smoothed
— remaining 75 mm concrete left rough
— 75 mm concrete
— 230 mm hardcore

SECOND DAY — 600 mm x 450 mm cardboard box filled with soil
— new concrete poured round box

PLAN — 600 mm — 1800 mm
concrete 3 : 1 : 1 gravel : sand : cement
600 mm x 450 mm x 600 mm deep boxes files with soil

81   Construction of an underground concrete water tank to hold approximately 1,365 litres (after Hills, 1971).

systems of water purification are applicable on a small scale, although the equipment and methods used are much less sophisticated and specialized than those used for large-scale water treatment.

The initial stage of screening and sedimentation is designed to remove suspended solids. The screening removes the larger particles from the collected water. If the water were from a roof, the particles would consist mainly of bird droppings and dust, but if it were drawn from a stream, larger items such as leaves and twigs would have to be removed. The value of screening is reflected by a reduction in the load for the later stages of treatment; a series of screens ranging from a grille of metal bars to a micromesh will remove much of the material normally deposited in the later stages. However, very small meshes will require cleaning often if they are not to block the system, and for this reason a sedimentation tank can be introduced to share part of the load of the screening system so that maintainance can be reduced. Either the

150

sedimentation tank can be filled and left for a period of time, or the water can flow continuously through the tank at a much-reduced velocity so that the suspended solids may settle out under gravity. The suspended solids are particles of silt, clay, sand and organic matter which have been caught up in the turbulent flow of rivers or of rainfall through gutters and carried along in suspension by the water-flow. On the large scale, continuous-flow sedimentation tanks are generally used as they require less space. These are designed so that the water passes through them in a smooth, even, turbulence-free manner. The precipitation of the suspended solids is often assisted by chemicals which coagulate the particles until a dense particle is formed which sinks to the bottom of the tank at a much faster rate. Aluminium sulphate in doses varying from 0.2 to 1.2 grains per litre of water is very effective for this purpose, provided that it is thoroughly mixed.

However, it may not be possible or necessary to introduce a continuous-flow sedimentation tank into the domestic system. If the rainwater is screened and stored before purification, a proportion of the suspended solids will settle out before the water is pumped to a secondary filtration process. The system described (see fig. 79) for developing countries uses only screens, filters and sterilization for purification, although the addition of a settling tank would relieve the load on the filter and hence prolong its life. Such a tank also helps to even the flow across the filter (fig. 82). Since the detention time

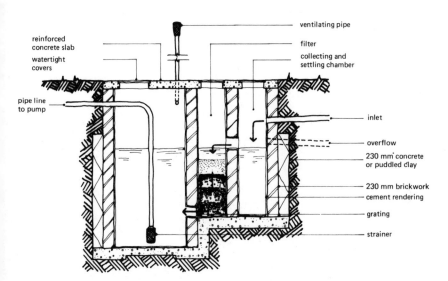

82   *Rainwater storage tank with filter incorporated (after Goodin and Downing, 1959).*

for large-scale settling tanks varies from 3 to 24 hours, depending on whether a coagulant is used, 24 hours would probably be a sufficient length of time to detain the rainwater before it passes to the secondary stage of treatment.

The process of good filtration removes the majority of suspended solids and bacteria and is therefore very important in the treatment of water. The slow percolation of water through beds of sand and graded gravel is the oldest method of water purification on a large scale known in Britain, and has a successful history. Although pressure filters are now widely used for public supplies, slow sand filtration continues to provide excellent protection against water-borne infection in many areas. A home-made filter should, however, always be used in conjunction with some tertiary treatment before the water is drunk, although tertiary treatment is probably not necessary for water for washing or laundry, provided that it cannot accidentally be used for drinking.

In the past, attempts have been made to improve the domestic water supply with home-made filters of animal or vegetable charcoal, sandstone or filter cloths. In a reprint of an old American farming magazine (*Mother Earth News*, 1972) a filter is described for a farm which, with no well or surface water supply, was forced to collect and use all the rainwater that fell on the house. The filter (see fig. 83) was made of an

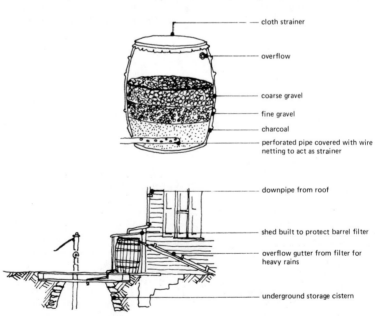

83   *Old-fashioned charcoal filter, not recommended for use. Reprinted in* Mother Earth News *(1972).*

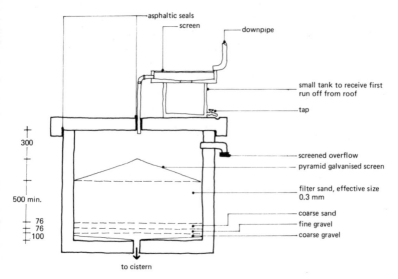

300

500 min.

76
76
100

to cistern

84 Slow sand filter with diversion for the first run-off from the roof (after Village Technology Handbook, *1970). The screen helps to distribute the water over the surface of the sand so that it does not make holes in it. To avoid water overflowing the filter the filter area should not be less than one-tenth of the catchment area.*

old barrel with one end removed. A layer of fine charcoal was placed at the base of the barrel, covered with a layer of fine gravel, over which was a layer of coarse gravel and, on the top of the barrel, a thin cloth strainer held in place with a hoop. The strainer acted as a screen to catch the leaves and dirt and was supposed to be cleaned after every shower. The positioning of the barrel filter is also shown in fig. 83. It was reported to have worked successfully. However, its chief benefit would be in cleaning the rainwater to render it visually rather than bacterially pure. If not cleaned regularly, such a filter may even have increased the bacterial content of the water. Such filters are a hazard as the water appears clean and can only be shown to be unfit for drinking if proper tests are carried out.

Bacterial purity can be achieved by passing the water through a slow sand filter. These can be made for the home, and the filter is built up of layers of material in much the same way as the filter described above (fig. 84). The top layer of fine sand is kept flooded to a depth of 300 mm with the water to be filtered. The fine sand should be a clean, fine quartz of 0.5 − 0.25 mm diameter. The layer under this is a coarser sand, then a fine gravel and lastly a coarse gravel, the coarser material in the lower part preventing the sand from being washed through into the stream of purified water. Under normal conditions the

153

rate of filtration should not exceed 90 – 140 litres per square metre of filter surface area per hour, or a vertical velocity of 100 mm/hour.

After first being set up the sand filter is only effective in removing the suspended matter by acting as a strainer but, as the suspended matter settles on the surface of the bed, an active biological growth forms in the top 75 mm of sand. The growth, known as the *Schmutzdecke* (dirt layer), consists of algae, bacteria and protozoan organisms together with finely divided material, plankton and other organic matter, all of which combine together to form an extremely fine-mesh straining mat. More particles and up to 95 per cent of the bacteria are trapped as the water is slowed down through this mat. This layer of growth is protected by the 300 mm of water constantly flooding the filter surface. A continuous flow of water should be maintained through the filter, as the micro-organisms will be destroyed if the sand dries out. It is also best to keep the filter covered and in the dark, but air must be allowed to circulate above the sand to help the biological growth develop. With continuous operation of the filter the growth builds up and

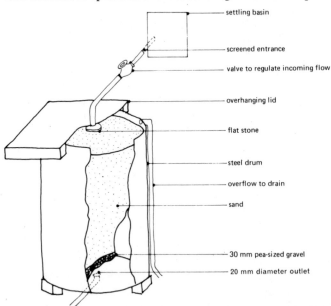

85   Trickling sand filter for a constant water supply such as a stream (after Village Technology Handbook, *1970). The entrance from the settling basin is screened to prevent clogging and to relieve the load on the filter. The overhanging lid prevents dust and rain from entering but allows air to circulate above the sand, and a flat stone under the inflow avoids the formation of a crater in the sand. There should be at least 600 mm of sand, but 750 mm or more would be better. The outlet pipe should be connected closely to the container in order to keep out insects and dust.*

154

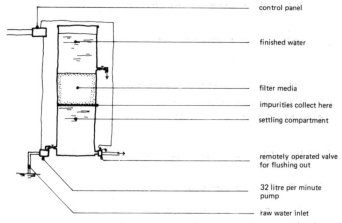

control panel

finished water

filter media

impurities collect here

settling compartment

remotely operated valve for flushing out

32 litre per minute pump

raw water inlet

86 Automated upflow filter for domestic water supplies (after Daniel and Garton, 1967). This experimental water filter for domestic use is designed to avoid the need for the user to scrape off the layer of impurities which collects on the top surface of a conventional gravity-feed sand filter. Once a week the bottom valve is opened by a time clock and the treated water is allowed to flow down through the filter media, thus removing the layer of impurities. This operation uses between 5 and 8 per cent of the filtered water requirements of an average family. The level of finished water in the upper tank is controlled by water-level sensors which operate the pump as required. To improve the effectiveness of the unit a coagulant (alum) and a sterilizing agent (chlorine) are added automatically to the raw water before it enters the settling compartment.

eventually becomes clogged. The filter must then be cleaned by scraping off and discarding the top 5 mm of sand, after which the surface should be lightly raked or scratched. Ideally, a new biological growth should be allowed to develop before the water from the cleaned filter bed is used, especially if no tertiary treatment is being used, and for this reason it is best to have two filters. The second filter also means that there is no shortage of supply during the cleaning periods. The filter will probably need cleaning once every several weeks or even months, but it should be left until the flow through can no longer meet the daily requirements, so that the biological growth is disturbed as little as possible. After several cleanings, fresh sand should be added to raise the bed to its original height, the old bed having first been scraped down to a clean level.

As mentioned above, the sand filter is most effective where the supply of water is continuous, as when it is taken from a stream, so that the sand filter is kept wet and oxygenated to keep the biological layer healthy and active. Where rainwater is fed directly through a filter into a storage tank, the filter will only be flooded at intervals, and so fewer bacteria will be prevented from passing through it. This problem might be avoided by collecting, screening and storing the rainwater and then feeding it to the filter through a pump, thus creating a continuous flow

155

artificially, although the pump would then require an addition of energy to the system. It might be possible to construct a slow upflow sand filter to solve these problems (see fig. 86). The biological layer is kept active by the water above it, and the filter can easily be cleaned by letting some of this stored water run out quickly through the filter under gravity, thus cleaning without destroying the biologically active layer. It is possible to achieve high rates of flow with a filter of this type.

Sterilization is the final phase of purification and is intended to remove all undesirable bacteria, particularly those capable of transmitting disease; it should be carried out for all drinking waters, even when these have been filtered and therefore have a high level of organic purity. The simplest method of sterilization is by boiling for 5 minutes, which kills all bacteria. However, boiling also drives off all the dissolved gases, leaving the water flat and tasteless, although allowing it to stand covered in the partially-filled container it was boiled in will help to rectify this. Most authorities agree that boiled water is only unsatisfactory for drinking because of the taste, but British Berkfeld Filters maintain that not all the spores of the bacteria are killed by boiling, and those remaining can become active once the water has cooled. Boiling is also an energy-consuming process.

In large treatment plants, sterilization of drinking water is carried out by adding chemicals. The commonest method is the addition of a very small quantity of chlorine to the water, but it is quite difficult to scale down this treatment to a domestic supply. The chlorine is usually added in the form of a gas at the treatment works, but on the domestic scale the process is only possible if it is added in the form of a solution such as Milton, which contains 1 per cent available chlorine, or a home-made solution of 39 cc of bleaching powder dissolved in 1 litre of water to give a 1 per cent solution. The water to be sterilized is treated by adding 3 drops of the 1 per cent solution to each litre, after which the chlorinated water should be mixed thoroughly and then left for at least 30 minutes before drinking. After this time, the water should be tested for the presence of 'free' chlorine. When chlorine is added to the water it attacks all organic matter, whether dead or alive, and some minerals such as iron if these are present. Enough chlorine must therefore be added to oxidize all these and leave some residual chlorine so that the water can be stored without risk of recontamination. There are orthotolidine kits available for testing that free chlorine is present in treated water. It can be seen that the process is perhaps too complicated for domestic use.

Other large-scale tertiary treatment methods are even less attractive from the point of view of scaling them down. Ozone, which is a

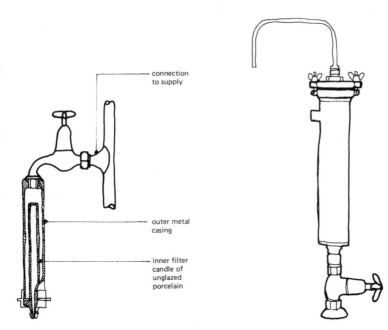

connection
to supply

outer metal
casing

inner filter
candle of
unglazed
porcelain

87   Two domestic water filters. (Left) Pasteur Chamberland domestic filter
(after Goodin and Downing, 1959). A candle of unglazed porcelain is contained within a metal casing connected directly to a bib valve. Water passes
through the filter walls from outside to inside. The filtration rate is therefore
slow and the candle needs sterilizing by boiling. (Right) Sink-mounting silver-
impregnated candle for use with pressure head of 7 metres to yield 113 litres/
hour (after British Berkfeld Filters Ltd). Water again passes through the candle
from outside to inside, but the impurities thus deposited on the candle surface
can be scrubbed off with a small brush.

powerful sterilizing agent, must be manufactured on the site where it
is to be used, and leaves no sterilizing residue in the water, which can
therefore become recontaminated before use. Ultra-violet light has also
been used for water sterilization. The water is passed over an ultra-
violet lamp, care being taken to ensure that the water is no more than
75 mm deep as the ultra-violet light will not penetrate and destroy
bacteria at a greater depth. Problems occur with keeping the surface of
the lamp free from deposits, the presence of which lowers the efficiency
of the system. Reverse osmosis, freeze desalination and ion exchange
are other tertiary treatment systems too expensive or impractical for
domestic use.

   The simplest method of sterilization is to pass the water through a
filter candle impregnated with colloidal or activated silver, which
produces water of a high bacteriological purity. The candle is a hollow
cylinder, the water passing from outside to inside. Silver has been used

157

as a sterilizing medium since pre-Roman times, although the mechanism of its effectiveness is still not really understood. However, the silver is non-toxic and imparts no taste or odour to the water. The treated water can also be stored without becoming contaminated with bacteria. Ceramic filter candles can also be used for sterilizing. They incorporate kieselguhr, a diatomaceous earth, which acts as a very fine filter excluding all solid particles down to 2 microns in diameter, which is sufficient to eliminate harmful bacteria. The water can be allowed to trickle through either type of candle under gravity, yielding a maximum of 55 litres of treated water in 24 hours, which may be too little for household demands. Alternatively, pressure filters, either fitted with pumps or having an equivalent head of 7 m of water, can supply over 450 litres an hour. The exterior of the filter candle gradually clogs up and the candles should therefore be cleaned, with a brush if they are of the silver-impregnated type, or by boiling, every 1 − 2 months. A filter candle has a life of about two years.

The only other method of obtaining pure water on the domestic scale is by distillation using solar energy. The first solar still was built in Chile in 1872, and it distilled salt water successfully at a nitrate mine for 40 years until the mine was exhausted. Although water is purified on a large scale by non-solar distillation, the large amounts of energy necessary for this treatment would probably be unobtainable in an autonomous situation where energy is at a premium. However, solar energy can easily be used for distilling water, and its intermittent nature is no real drawback as long as storage for the distilled water is provided so that the supply can be maintained when the sun is not shining. The still is made by filling a shallow, black-painted or lined container with the water to be purified, which is then covered with a sloping sheet of glass. The solar energy is absorbed by the black surface, the temperature of which is raised. The water is heated in turn and evaporates. The water vapour rises, comes into contact with the cooler sheet of glass and condenses, running down the incline to be collected in a separate trough. Although bacterial purity of water can be achieved by use of a filter candle, distillation is the only method of removing the heavy metal contaminants of rainwater, such as the large amount of lead it contains in London, which might otherwise accumulate in the body to cause a serious health hazard. A solar still (see fig. 88) was successfully used in the Ecol operation at McGill University. It was used for distilling water which had already been used for showering, the distilled water, once collected, forming the only source of water for drinking and cooking. Here the solar still was made of a black-lined asbestos cement tray, and different configurations for the glass covering the tray were tried (see fig. 89). From 5 September to 5 October 1972 the Ecol still produced

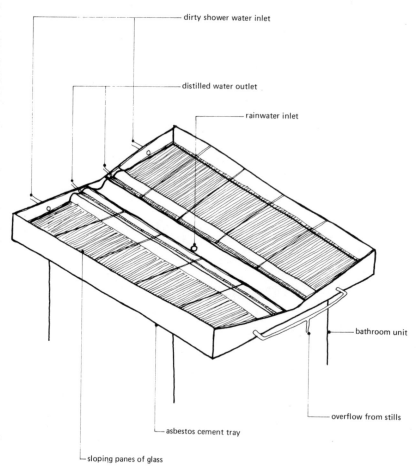

88　*The solar still which formed the roof of the bathroom unit in the Ecol house at McGill University (after Ortega* et al., *1972).*

395 litres of purified water, of which 368 litres were used for drinking, cooking and washing. Smith (1973) estimates that, for Britain, 11 m^2 of solar still would be needed to distil an average 15 litres a day throughout the year (1.2 kWh of solar incidence per litre of water distilled, but this would probably be nearer to 2 kWh/litre in practice), though this production would vary from 5 litres a day in December to 35 litres a day or more in June.

To overcome this, it might be possible to store distilled water from season to season. Although such a still could also be arranged to collect rainwater, if it were mounted on the roof of the house the over-all area

159

A solar still made of a moulded asbestos-cement tray with a cover of two panes of glass. The panes are connected along their edges with silicone applied by a gun. Wet polythene placed between the panes prevents the silicone from sticking. After 12 hours the silicone is set but it is flexible enough to allow the two panes of glass to fold like a hinge.

The type of still used at the ECOL house. Here the panes of glass are fixed to the outside edges of the tray and slope inwards, the water being collected in a trough fixed at the lowest point.

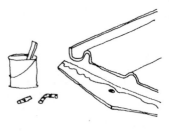

The ends of the still can also be made of asbestos-cement and holes have to be drilled in these to take the plastic spigots for the supply pipes and overflow. The asbestos-cement ends can then be glued in place with a two-component epoxy glue.

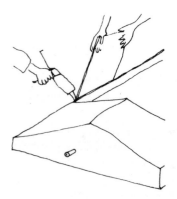

The glass panes are then fixed in place to form a cover with silicone as described.

89   *Construction of a simple solar still (after an article in* International Asbestos-cement Review, *1973).*

160

of any other solar collector for water or space heating would be reduced, with a consequent reduction in the amount of energy that could be collected for these purposes. However, Smith suggests that it might also be possible to combine the two functions by using an open Thomason-type collector (see p. 39) where any evaporating water condenses on the clear covering sheet and could be collected. Combining the functions, however, probably reduces the efficiency of both systems. The condensed droplets increase the reflectivity of the clear covering sheets, and so less solar energy passes through to be absorbed. At the same time, the increased size of the 'still' means that much of the condensate will drip back into the flow of water before being collected, and only that forming at the bottom of the collector will be caught in the trough. Nevertheless, it might still be possible to collect sufficient distilled water in this way, and Thomason has demonstrated that this type of collector can heat water even if the efficiency is not so high. More experimental data is needed before such a system can really be assessed.

The Ecol solar still has demonstrated a method of purifying waste water and hence reducing the water collection requirements by recycling. Because of the quantities and the energy involved, it would be impractical to purify all water by distillation. It might be possible to treat waste waters chemically and by filtration so that washing and laundry wastes could be re-used continuously, topped up occasionally with fresh water to make up evaporation losses and wastage. On the large scale, soapy laundry wastes have been treated with sulphuric acid to bring the pH to 6.4 − 6.6, and coagulants such as alum or ferric sulphate to remove 70 − 80 per cent of the polluting matter, about 5 per cent of the water being lost as sludge. This sludge could be collected and digested anaerobically without harming the bacterial balance in the fermentation tank. However, since rainwater is very soft, the amount of soap-based detergent used would be small. The water, once treated chemically, could then be passed through a slow sand filter to improve its bacteriological quality and appearance. Although natural soap and straight-chain synthetic detergents such as Teepol can be oxidized biochemically in a filter, the initial chemical treatment improves the final purity of the water and also relieves the load on the filter, hence prolonging its life. The filtered water would probably be satisfactory for laundry and bathing, although if it were used for washing dishes a health hazard could result.

Recently, claims have been made for the benefits of distributing waste bath and laundry water directly on to the garden; although recycling of water could not then be achieved, the amount consumed would theoretically be reduced, as this water would be used twice. This would allow the rainwater collection area to be expanded to include

161

greenhouse roofs or even artificial collectors over the garden. The collected and treated water would then be used in the house before being collected again as soapy waste water and distributed on the garden. However, the value of such water to the garden has not been firmly established, and some opinion suggests that it is in fact harmful to plants. The argument is based on the fact that synthetic detergents, in addition to the surface-active content which provides the lather and cleansing action, also contain 'builders' which are usually a mixture of sodium salts, phosphates, carbonates, sulphates, silicates and perborates. When the detergent-filled water enters a river, the phosphates act as a fertilizer, causing a rapid increase in the growth of algae. These in turn consume the oxygen out of the water, causing fish to die. However, a case has been made for the beneficial qualities of phosphates as a plant fertilizer. Searle (1970) in his trials at his home claims that the soapy water enabled 'plants to extract water from the soil more easily. In no case had soapy water ruined or killed any plants. The bacteria in the soil appear to thrive on it, and the earthworms living in soapy areas are as healthy as ever.' However, other detergent components such as whiteners may have a harmful effect as they accumulate in the soil. At the same time, the run-off from the garden and the percolation of the soapy water through the soil will carry phosphates with them, and if these enter a watercourse or lake the whole pollution problem is started again. Since there is no real evidence to support either argument, it would be best to seek other methods of recycling water and disposing of the waste water.

The re-use of water, rather than recycling, may be a better way of approaching the problem, apart from the introduction of measures to save water. Obvious savings could be made by using a shower rather than a bath as an adequate shower takes only 5 − 15 litres of water. Amounts of water for personal hygiene are difficult to assess as individuals' requirements vary so widely. It has been stated that if every person in Britain bathed once a week, there would be a serious water shortage. A Japanese-style bath could reduce the water needed for bathing, as here a cleansing shower precedes the soak in the warm water, the same water being shared by all the family. This water is stored in a wooden tub, and covered with a wooden lid when not in use to keep it hot. It is often heated in a pillow-type solar collector, being drained into the tub in the evening. If it were pumped back to the collector through a filter candle, which would thus clean it quickly, the water could be used several times with an over-all saving in consumption. Mists and sprays, as proposed by Buckminster Fuller (Pike, 1965), would reduce consumption for personal hygiene. The Ecol operation experimented with a Japanese atomizer, operated with a foot pedal,

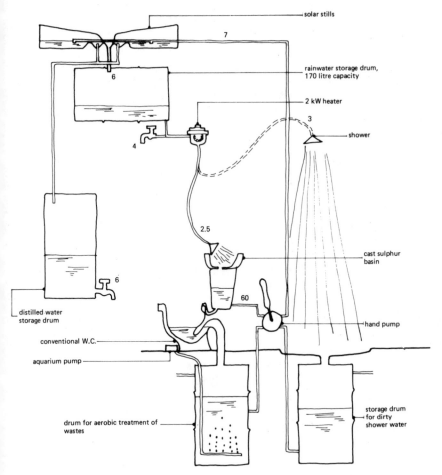

Labels in figure (clockwise / as positioned):
- solar stills
- 7
- 6
- rainwater storage drum, 170 litre capacity
- 2 kW heater
- 3
- shower
- 4
- 2.5
- cast sulphur basin
- 6
- 60
- distilled water storage drum
- hand pump
- conventional W.C.
- aquarium pump
- drum for aerobic treatment of wastes
- storage drum for dirty shower water

90   The Ecol water collection, purification and waste treatment system (after Ortega et al., *1972). The figures show the quantities, in litres per head, passing through the system per day.*

which provided 22 hand-washes from one filling of 0.2 litre. Pressure-cooking could be used in the kitchen to conserve both water and energy, and ultrasonic cleaning has been suggested as a replacement for conventional laundry methods.

It might be more practical for the present to aim for some degree of autonomy by trying to balance water needs against the water collected plus the water savings that can be easily accomplished. At the same time, instead of cutting down demands by complicated repurification between each use, a system could be established of using water of different

163

standards of purity for different purposes, as in the earlier example where the conventional W.C. was flushed with waste bathwater. The water must also be considered in terms of the energy needed to heat it for washing, laundry and dishes, and the possibility of recovering the waste heat afterwards. The water system thus becomes an integral part of the heating, cooking and sewage systems of the house. The following example shows some proposed systems of this type for use on the domestic scale.

The simplest and cheapest successfully tested system is that demonstrated in the Ecol house at McGill University (see fig. 90). Here three water purities are introduced. Collected rainwater is stored and used for washing hands, showering and hair-washing. The hand-basin is situated in the top of the W.C. cistern, and this water is used for flushing as well. It then mixes with the sewage and is fermented aerobically, aeration of the tank being achieved with a small aquarium pump. The water can then be pumped back up to the cistern and used for W.C. flushing. The dirty shower-water is collected and stored before being pumped up to the solar still, where the distillate is collected and used for cooking and drinking. The quantities of water involved in this system, which was used by two people, are indicated on the diagram.

At a more sophisticated level, the Grumman Corporation have developed an integrated household waste and water system based on their experience of designing life-support systems for astronauts. The system (see fig. 91) is based on the assumption that washing machines, dishwashers etc. will continue to be used, and that the owners of the house will be too conservative to use recycled water for cooking, drinking or dish-washing. As shown, the daily input of 1,050 litre/day is only slightly less than that of 1,140 litre/day for a conventional American house (washing and kitchen 130 litres, laundry and bathing 550 litres, W.C. 460 litres), so very little saving is apparently being made. However, of these 1,050 litres, 670 litres of clean mains water are placed directly on the garden and only 380 litres are used and treated within the house. The mains water supply is used directly in the sink, basin and dish-washer. Thence it passes through a biological waste-treatment unit, and mixes with mains water to supply the washing machine, shower and bath. Waste heat from the water- and sewage-treatment process, together with heat from a refuse incinerator, is used to bring about evaporation in an air-evaporator unit which acts as an air conditioner to the house, the heat being released on condensation. The system has been constructed around this air-evaporator unit and the sophisticated secondary sewage-treatment plant without real thought as to the purpose or significance of the whole system. The principles were modified by Smith (1973) to produce a system more

164

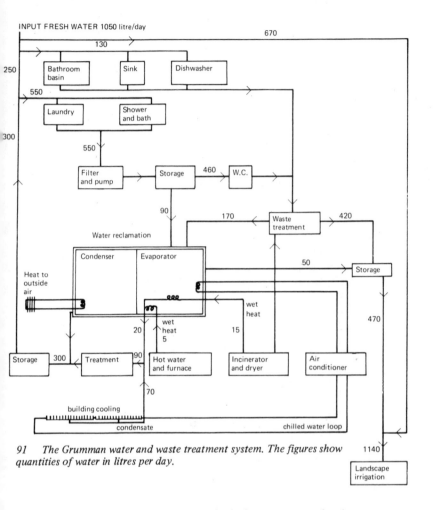

91 *The Grumman water and waste treatment system. The figures show quantities of water in litres per day.*

suited to an autonomous situation in which the water input has been reduced to 80 litre/day. However, the large energy input also needed to run such a system might be excessive for the autonomous situation.

The system designed for the Westinghouse Homelab at the Westinghouse Research Laboratory, Pittsburgh (see fig. 93) cuts the fresh water input down to 40 litre/day, which in the present experiment comes from the mains supply. This is used for drinking and cooking. The water for dish-washers, washing machines, bath, washbasin, shower and kitchen sink comes from a closed loop in which the wastes are purified by the principles of flotation and reverse osmosis for 15 cycles of use. The W.C. waste and flushing water are also incorporated into a separate closed cycle, which is designed to deal with the sewage from a family of four people without attention for one year. The sewage

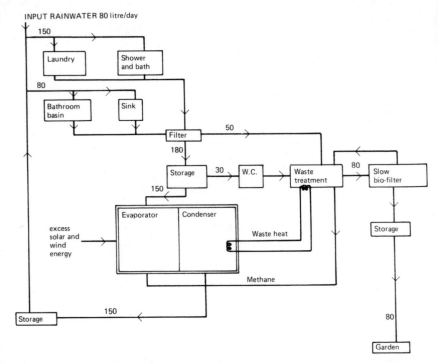

92   A modified Grumman system, more suitable for the autonomous house (after Smith, 1973). The figures show quantities of water in litres per day.

and flushing water pass to a tank where aerobic digestion breaks down the solids. The liquids which accumulate are passed through a carbon filter, chlorinated, and pumped to a storage tank which feeds the W.C. cistern. An ultra-violet lamp is installed in the top of the cistern as an additional precaution. The constant addition of urine and the evaporation within the system maintain the volume of liquid at a reasonably constant level. The yearly maintenance would be for the removal of the sludge layer at the bottom of the tank, although Westinghouse hope to fit a sludge incinerator so that the only output is a small quantity of ash. Again, energy is needed for pumps, aeration and the reverse osmosis unit.

The last system was designed as part of an autonomous house project (Vale, 1973) and attempted to produce a simple, low-energy system where normal water consumption was supplied and the wastes recycled (see fig. 94). The rainwater is collected, screened and stored before being pumped to feed a slow sand filter. The drinking and cooking water is then sterilized by passing through a silver-impregnated filter candle. The filtered cold water feeds a low-flush W.C. and some is also

166

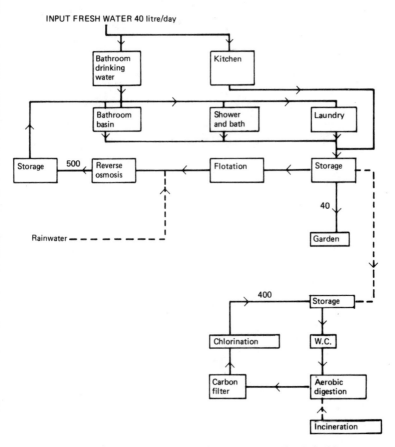

93 *The Westinghouse water and waste treatment system. The dashed lines
indicate possible future interconnections; the figures show quantities of water
in litres per day.*

used for adjusting the water content of the methane digester. The
remainder feeds into a hot-water storage tank where it is warmed by
solar energy to form the hot-water supply of the house. The warm
waste water from washing etc. flows to a tank under the methane
digester so that some waste heat can be reclaimed from it. It is then
treated with approximately 0.06 litre of alum to precipitate out many
of the pollutants before being pumped back through the sand filter to
feed the hot-water system. Only purified rainwater is used for drinking.
The system demonstrates that, without attempts at water saving, the
process of water recycling is complicated and a large amount of
equipment is needed, only some of which duplicates the standard cold-
and hot-water system for a house with mains input.

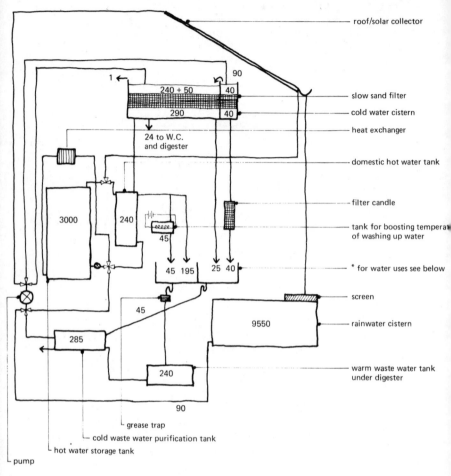

- roof/solar collector
- slow sand filter
- cold water cistern
- heat exchanger
- domestic hot water tank
- filter candle
- tank for boosting temperature of washing up water
- * for water uses see below
- screen
- rainwater cistern
- warm waste water tank under digester
- grease trap
- cold waste water purification tank
- hot water storage tank
- pump

*45 litres for washing up
195 litres for baths and personal hygiene
25 litres for laundry
40 litres for drinking and food preparation

94   *Hot and cold water system for Autonomous House 1. The figures show the daily quantity of water, in litres, for a family of four.*

At the end of the chapter we show seven different systems, and the approximate rainwater collection areas they would need, plotted against average annual rainfall. In most of the systems, the lower water consumption depends on energy being introduced to achieve some degree of water-recycling. If water requirements cannot be met by rainwater collection then some other method, such as extracting moisture from the atmosphere by dehumidification, might be resorted to, although here again energy would be needed to produce water. The balance between water and energy is becoming more critical on the large scale and it has become apparent that increasing demands for water will lead to increasing demands for energy: 'recent successes with the breeder reactor offer exciting prospects of unlimited energy supplies, which through desalination would yield unlimited water supplies' (*Natural Resources Research*, 1968).

In some parts of Britain, rainfall supplies are adequate to supply all needs, and so water purification and some treatment of waste water are the only problems. In many places, especially in the decentralized autonomous community, surface water or even wells may be used for the supply, although in any general assessment of the problem it is probably better to consider rainfall only. Where rainfall is low, energy may have to be substituted for water, and it is fortunate that the areas of Britain having the highest numbers of hours of sunshine are also the driest parts of the country. Of course, savings in water can be made by the use of atomizing equipment or by cleaning and recycling water. The Ecol operation showed that, where the need for water-saving was apparent, the actual consumption for personal hygiene and laundry was 9.3 litre/head/day rather than 60 litre/head/day, the average for Britain, or 78 litre/head/day, the average for America, despite the fact that a conventional shower and hand-basin were used. The addition of animals to such an autonomous situation exacerbates the problem as animals considerably increase the demand for drinking water (especially if they are milk-producers), even though the roofs of their housing can be added to the total collection area. It may be that, where the water-versus-energy situation is critical, food, too, may enter into the discussion, and animal protein (milk, pork, lamb) may have to be replaced with vegetable or small-animal protein (beans, eggs, rabbit).

Bearing in mind that some form of regular monitoring of the supply is as important for small-scale plants as for large, the safest and most practical of the systems used for treating water would seem to be the slow sand filter, followed by solar distillation. Although the latter requires energy, it is possible to store the distilled water carefully, so the solar energy can be used when it is at a maximum. The filter candle operates successfully as a water-sterilization agent where the water to be treated is clear and bright, and Twort (1963) states that the silver content of the filtered water is too small to have any toxic effect on the consumer, even if it is drunk for a lifetime. However, a filter candle must be replaced every two years, whereas a solar still, once installed, is relatively permanent. On the other hand, there seems to be no real reason to purify rainwater that is only going to be used for laundry and personal hygiene excluding teeth-cleaning, and reasons of danger to children from this source seem rather over-protective. The W.C. in the autonomous house is best visualized as a new piece of equipment flushing with a very small quantity of water, probably water that has already been used for washing, or with recycled effluent. The W.C. in turn is connected up to some form of sewage-treatment system, either aerobic or anaerobic (methane digester, septic tank), which produces an effluent disposed of over an absorption field or, in the case of methane, a sludge which provides plants with both water and fertilizer. Thus the design of any water collection and purification system for a household must be considered as a balance between energy and water, collection area, equipment and consumption, animal protein and vegetable protein, and at the same time it must be integrated with the heating and sewage-treatment systems to form a complete servicing structure.

Rainwater collection and use systems for autonomous houses

The following theoretical systems range from the limit where no water is recycled and all waste water and sewage pass through a septic tank to an absorption field, to one in which water consumption is reduced to a minimum. The points at which energy has to be put into each system are shown. All figures are in litres/head/day.

System 1 – minimum consumption

Drinking and cooking water	5	
Dish-washing with an atomizer	0.3	
Bath and basin using atomizers and recycling the water 15 times	0.06	energy
Laundry recycled 15 times	0.3	energy
W.C. self-contained system	–	energy
TOTAL	5.66	

Atomizers were used in the Ecol system for dish- and hand-washing. They reduced the consumption for hand washing from 0.5 litre to 0.01 litre, a 50 to 1 reduction. Buckminster Fuller estimates that, with a fog gun, a bath would take only 0.5 litre rather than the 25 litres used for a conventional shower or 150 litres for a conventional bath, which gives at least a 50 to 1 reduction in consumption. The conventional values for personal hygiene and dishes have therefore been reduced by a factor of 50. At the same time, the water for personal hygiene has been recycled 15 times, the limit achieved by the Westinghouse system, and the daily value has therefore been reduced by a further factor of 15. The W.C. is a separate system such as the Westinghouse (see fig. 93) or Boester sewerless W.C., where the lavatory pan is flushed with the purified effluent from the system. Laundry water is recycled but not reduced, by using some specialized equipment. Ultrasonic washing machines which would eliminate water use have been proposed but are not yet available. The drinking and cooking water consumption has been kept at the average value of 5 litre/head/day, although the physiological need is only about 2 litre/head/day. Energy is needed to effect the recycling process and also to operate the separate sewage-treatment system. It is assumed that the atomizers could be operated by some mechanical means. Extra water might be needed to top up any evaporation losses in the recycling system.

System 2 – minimum consumption but using conventional taps

Drinking and cooking water	5	
Dish-washing	15	
Bath, basin and laundry, all recycled 15 times	4	energy
W.C. self-contained system	–	energy
TOTAL	24	

Some provision would have to be made for filtering the dirty dish-washing water before it could be disposed of on the garden. It might be possible to include this water in the recycling system.

System 3 – the ECOL house

Drinking and cooking / Dish-washing } distilled	–	solar energy
Shower, basin and laundry	9.3	
W.C. self-contained system	–	energy
TOTAL	9.3	

The personal hygiene requirements and hence the total water collected must not be reduced too much or there will be insufficient dirty washing water to distil for drinking. The W.C. is flushed with the purified effluent topped up with dirty water from the basin. The energy required for this self-contained system is enough electricity to run an aquarium pump. Although the equipment is conventional, water is used more sparingly in this system than in an ordinary domestic situation as the need for water conservation has been recognized. A similar situation occurs on camp-sites, where water consumption drops immediately the water has to be carried around.

System 4 – Autonomous House Project using conventional taps and bath

Drinking and cooking	10	
Dish-washing	11	
Bath, basin and laundry, all recycled	–	pump, chemicals
W.C. and methane digester	6	
TOTAL	27	

It is probably impossible to recycle the bath and laundry water continuously. If 15 repeats of the cycle could be achieved with the methods suggested, the total daily consumption increases to 31 litre/head/day. The value of 10 for drinking and food preparation is probably above average and the value of 11 for dish-washing rather low, but overall these two quantities balance. No allowance has been made for evaporation losses in the recycling system, but water is removed from the methane gas before it is used for cooking, and an additional water supply might be obtained from this source.

System 5 – a reappraisal of the above system including provision of water for animals

Drinking and cooking } distilled	–	solar energy
Dish-washing } 20/litre/head/day		
Shower, basin	15	
Bath, Japanese-type, water recycled 15 times	2.5	
Laundry	15	
W.C. and methane digester 6		
Goat (2)	12.5	
Hens (12)	0.75	
TOTAL	45.75	

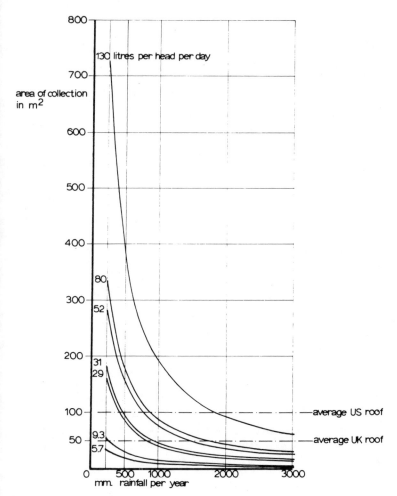

95   Graph relating rainwater collection area and rainfall for different daily litre/head consumption.

The 20 litres a head per day for drinking, cooking and dish-washing is distilled from the 30 l/h/d shower and laundry water. 6 l/h/d of this dirty water is used to flush the W.C. and for the digester, the soap contents having no deleterious effect on the bacteria. The water for the animals is worked out on a litre/person/day basis assuming a family of four and the numbers of animals shown above. The water for them is stored rainwater passed through a sand filter, while rainwater is used directly for showering and laundry.

System 6 – no recycling of water

Drinking and cooking	5
Dish-washing	15
Bath and basin	45
Laundry	15
W.C.	50
TOTAL	130

No energy is introduced into this system at all. The rainwater must be collected and filtered (sand filter and filter candle) before being used for drinking, cooking and dish-washing. All waste water passes through a septic tank and then through an absorption field.

System 7 – simple recycling

Drinking and cooking	5
Dish-washing	15
Bath and basin	45
Laundry	15
W.C.	–
TOTAL	80

The W.C. is flushed with waste bath and laundry water, which can be pumped up to the cistern with a hand or foot pump. Dish-washing and drinking water must again be collected and filtered before use. The dirty water and sewage pass through a septic tank to an absorption field.

7 Batteries and fuel cells

Unlike solar energy, maximum usable wind power occurs during periods when the demand for electricity is greatest, that is during winter nights. However, some storage capacity must be provided for periods without any wind, and at present batteries are the only viable solution to this problem. Research is now going on into new forms of batteries with longer life and higher storage capacity in order to provide an alternative to the internal combustion engine in cars by transferring the pollution from the streets to the power station, and into fuel cells to give power during space flights. The abundant supplies of fossil fuels and electricity generated from them have meant that the problem of the long-life stationary battery dealing with domestic capacities has not been investigated to any extent. Hence batteries for use with windmills have to be selected from the ranges available for other purposes. The types which have most practical and commercial value are lead-acid batteries and alkaline batteries, the latter including nickel-iron and nickel-cadmium assemblies.

The cheapest and most widely used batteries suitable for use as wind-power storage are lead-acid cells. However, apart from the capital cost, the life of any battery is also important in selecting a suitable type. The lead-acid cell, as found in all cars, consists of a positive electrode of lead dioxide in plate form and a negative electrode plate of spongy lead, both immersed in an electrolyte of dilute sulphuric acid. Despite the high weight involved, the lead-acid battery has the lowest initial and operating costs of all the various storage batteries, and the voltage on discharge is the highest of all the reversible combinations. The materials used in its construction are relatively plentiful and cheap, although even in 1965 the battery industry consumed 30 per cent of the world lead output. However, it is possible to salvage and re-use the lead from old batteries. The lead-acid cell will also operate satisfactorily over a wide ambient temperature range. It thus possesses many properties which make it suitable for domestic use, especially as the battery will be stationary and weight penalty will not be incurred.

The lead-acid cell has been developed chiefly for use in cars to supply power for lighting, starting and ignition, and the starter motor has defined the size and type of battery. In a normal car, the starter motor is often rated at 120 amps or more and a large area of plate is necessary to supply such a heavy current, especially as this may have to be delivered at temperatures below zero, at which the electrochemical reactions in the cells are considerably slowed down. During the charge and discharge cycles of the battery, the positive plate is gradually worn away and a deposit of lead dioxide builds up in the bottom of the cell. As the plate wears thin, it becomes mechanically weaker and eventually distorts and buckles under its own weight. Alternatively, the deposits may build up in the bottom of the battery until they touch the plates and short them out.

Formerly, the stationary batteries that were used for stand-by power or the operation of switch gear in the electricity supply industry were given a longer life by increasing the thickness of the positive plate and providing a large space below the plates to accommodate the deposit. However, this was impractical for car batteries, which had to be easily transportable, and for police or army use, where built-in obsolescence was of no advantage, batteries used to be provided with drain cocks so that the deposit could be periodically flushed out. Although new types of tubular glass cells and flat-plate glass-wool cells have been developed for stationary use (see fig. 96), they are more expensive than the conventional lead-acid car battery and it is this type, therefore, which has most often been used as storage for windmills. However, the total number of charge and discharge cycles will affect the life of the battery, especially if it is ever in danger of being completely discharged during a windless period.

A typical lead-acid car battery might have a life of 10–400 complete discharge cycles (Barak, 1970), which might be increased to 500–1,000 if some way could be found of cleaning out the sludge. Alternatively, the glass-tube type of stationary battery would give about 1,200 complete discharge cycles with an expected life of 4 – 12 years, depending upon the frequency with which the battery was discharged, but this type of battery costs between four and five times as much as a car battery of similar capacity. In use with windmills it is likely that the batteries could become almost completely discharged fairly often during wind-less periods. To ensure long life, it would be best only to half-discharge the battery, which implies a doubling of the storage capacity and the capital costs.

In order to obtain longer life from batteries which are liable to overcharging or complete discharge, it might be better to use a

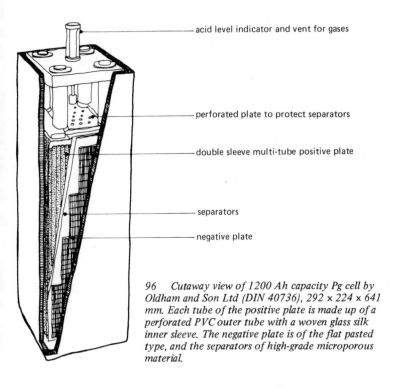

acid level indicator and vent for gases

perforated plate to protect separators

double sleeve multi-tube positive plate

separators

negative plate

96   *Cutaway view of 1200 Ah capacity Pg cell by Oldham and Son Ltd (DIN 40736), 292 × 224 × 641 mm. Each tube of the positive plate is made up of a perforated PVC outer tube with a woven glass silk inner sleeve. The negative plate is of the flat pasted type, and the separators of high-grade microporous material.*

different type of cell. Edison used plates of nickel hydroxide and iron, in an effort to reduce the weight of batteries rather than to prolong their life. Modern nickel-iron and nickel-cadmium batteries are able to stand idle at normal temperatures for long periods in various stages of charge without deterioration and with negligible loss of charge. Neither are they damaged by overcharging or complete discharge. This was admirably demonstrated by Harrods' London delivery vans, now superseded, which were fitted with nickel-iron batteries. These were recharged in seven hours or less at night, and completely discharged during the day over a 60-mile journey of stopping and delivering and climbing the steep crowded hills leading to Hampstead and Highgate. The active battery life on the vans was well over ten years, whereas lead-acid batteries used for traction have a normal active life of 5 – 6 years. The nickel-iron battery has an iron negative plate with a tubular nickel oxide positive plate, while the nickel-cadmium cell, developed by the Swedish scientist Jungner, uses a cadmium negative plate. Both types use a potassium hydroxide electrolyte which needs occasional topping up with distilled water. The alkaline batteries are somewhat limited in application, as they are twice the size of a lead-acid unit of equivalent

Table 14 Estimated properties of electrical energy storage cells

Cells	Typical temp. (°C)	Resistivity of electrolyte (Ω cm)	Cell voltage at discharge (V)
Lead-acid	40–50	1.53	2.1–1.46
Nickel-iron	0–40	1.96	1.3–0.75
Nickel-cadmium	40–60	1.96	1.3–0.75
Silver-zinc	0–40	1.96	1.55–1.1
Silver-cadmium	40–60	1.96	1.3–0.8
Lithium-chloride	650	0.17	3.40
Lithium-metal halide	25	–	2.1
Sodium-sulphur	300	5 (solid)	2.08–1.76
Sodium-air	130	3.58	2.3
Zinc-air	25	–	1.4
Sodium-bismuth	540–580	0.44	0.8–0.4
Lithium-tellurium	450–480	0.26	1.79–1.67

capacity and the raw materials used in their manufacture are much more expensive. Barak (1970) estimates that alkaline storage batteries cost 3 – 10 times as much as lead-acid batteries of equivalent storage capacity. The manufacturers of nickel-cadmium cells estimate that a battery of this type used in good conditions should have a useful working life of 20 –25 years. Under average conditions this would drop to 10 – 20 years and in the worst conditions, such as traction applications, where the battery goes through a daily charge/discharge cycle, a life of 8 years is expected. As the Harrods' vans demonstrated, these estimates are rather pessimistic.

Other types of cell are available or are being investigated for the storage of power. Most research is aimed at producing more storage capacity for less weight and volume, in order to improve the range of electric vehicles and eventually produce a viable electric car. Most systems so far devised, however, use materials which are scarcer than lead or even nickel, and hence the prices of the improved-capacity systems are very much higher. Silver-zinc cells are available on the market with capacities ranging from 0.1 Ah to 300 Ah, and they have an energy density three to six times higher than that of nickel-iron or nickel-cadmium cells. They consist of a silver oxide positive active material, and porous spongy zinc as the negative material, in an electrolyte of potassium hydroxide. However, the zinc is partially soluble in the electrolyte, and short circuits tend to develop after a limited number of cycles. This gives the cell only a short cycle life (see table 14), although cells of this type have a long storage life in the dry state. The cost of such batteries is at least ten times that of the lead-acid cell, and their use has therefore been restricted to military or space

Current density (A/cm^2)	Specific power (W/lb)	Specific energy (Wh/lb)	Shelf life discharged	Operating life cycles
0.010	3–14	8–14	None	10–400
–	3–18	14–16	Years	100–3000
0.010	3–20	16–18	Years	100–2000
0.43	11–68	36–45	Years	100–300
–	9–30	23–27	Years	500–1100
1–3	36–68	150	–	–
–	–	19	–	–
0.7	100	136	–	–
0.07	41	159	–	–
–	27	91	–	–
0.5–1	36	18	Years	> 500
2–5	127	82	Years	–

(After Barak, 1970)

use where cost is not so important. The silver-zinc cell is also damaged by overcharging. By using cadmium rather than zinc as the negative electrode, an increase in the number of charge/discharge cycles can be achieved, while the energy density is still two to three times that of conventional lead-acid batteries. However, the scarcity of both cadmium and silver make this a storage cell of still more limited application. Table 14 compares the energy densities of different cell systems.

Energy densities can also be improved by operating systems at higher temperatures. Work has been done in both Britain and America on a sodium-sulphur cell which, because the materials involved are very much lighter, has a projected energy density ten to twelve times greater than that of conventional storage cells. It would therefore be much more suitable for powering an electric car. However, the cell must be heated to about 500° C before the electrochemical reaction commences, although it is claimed that, once the discharge is started, the exothermic reaction will maintain the temperature. Insulation would then have to be provided which, by adding to the weight and bulk of the system, would make it less attractive. A prototype sodium-sulphur battery has already been installed in a Bedford van and is being tested at the Electricity Council Research Centre at Capenhurst, Cheshire. The ECRC estimates that it will be ready for mass production in five years, although they cannot predict whether it will be commercially competitive by then.

General Motors and others have been working on a lithium-chloride cell which would weigh fifteen times less than a lead-acid battery of similar capacity. The working temperature of the lithium-chloride cell is around 650° C. However, although the sodium-sulphur cell and the

179

lithium-chloride cell have high power densities and can be recharged quickly — advantageous features for application to electric vehicles — both are toxic in operation. It has also been difficult to find a non-aqueous electrolyte to be used in them. Research has therefore been directed towards making cells from the alkali metals with an organic electrolyte, the most promising results coming from a cell with lithium as the negative pole, propylene carbonate as the electrolyte and nickel fluoride as the depolarizer, with the fluoride ion supplied as the oxidant. A salt also has to be added to increase the conductivity of the cell. So far, these cells have found no practical application.

Of all the systems available or proposed, the lead-acid and nickel-iron or nickel-cadmium batteries are the only ones which have potential at present for the storage of wind-produced electricity, even though their efficiencies (power stored in relation to weight and volume) are low. The alkaline batteries have a nominal voltage of 1.2, rising to 1.4 V when fully charged and falling to 1.0 V at full discharge. However, these are penalized by being much more expensive than the lead-acid cells. The latter have a nominal voltage of 2.0, giving a working range from 2.2 V when fully charged down to 1.8 V at the safe discharge limit. However, an important characteristic of all storage batteries is the fact that they can be charged in parallel at low voltages of, say, 2 V from a wind generator and then discharged in series at a high voltage, giving greater efficiency in the operation of electrical equipment.

For estimating battery storage capacity in a practical way, the battery should be large enough to carry the electrical load for five days. If the windmill is large enough to supply power for ironing, a washing machine, etc., it is best to work out the total weekly loading as in the following example taken from the Wincharger operating manual, and then take 5/7 of the value to give the watt-hour load for five days:

light:	3 x 25-W bulbs for 4 hours	x 7	2,100 watt-hours a week
	3 x 50-W bulbs for 3 hours	x 7	3,150 Wh/week
radio:	10 W for 5 hours	x 7	350 Wh/week
washing:	275 W for 4 hours		1,100 Wh/week
iron:	600 W for 3 hours		1,800 Wh/week
	TOTAL		8,500 Wh/week

The storage capacity of the batteries should therefore be 6,070 watt-hours. Assuming that the battery complex is made up of 16 cells, each rated at 2 V, to give a total rating of 32 V, then the capacity of the battery selected should be 190 ampere-hours or slightly more. The ampere-hour ratings of stationary batteries given in manufacturers' leaflets usually refer to a 10-hour discharge period. This means that a battery rated at 200 ampere-hours with a 10-hour period of discharge will give a current of 20 amps for 10 hours, but it will not provide a current of 200 amps for 1 hour. The actual rate of discharge for one hour will be in the region of half the specified rate. Thus, when specifying batteries, care should be taken to ascertain what discharge period the ampere-hour rate refers to.

The manufacturer of the Wincharger No. D 32 V machine, now no longer made, also recommended that, where heavy appliances such as motors or irons were being used, heavy-duty farm lighting batteries should be used rather than cheaper, smaller batteries with thinner plates. Care of the lead-acid batteries was also important for obtaining a maximum life and, apart from checking the amount of charge in each cell with a hydrometer and keeping the cells topped up with distilled water to a level 12.5 mm above the plates, other methods were given for extending battery life. The batteries were never to be allowed to remain low of charge for any length of time and, should they become discharged, all lights and loads were to be turned off to allow all charge to enter the batteries. At the same time, if the drain on the batteries was very small and the battery was constantly being kept at full charge, it should be cycled about once a month. This entailed allowing the battery to become fully discharged and then charged again immediately. This cycling was recommended to keep the plates clean, and had to be done on a windy day so that the batteries soon resumed a full charge. Overcharging was recommended every three or four months, and this could be carried out by continuing the charging even when the hydrometer indicated that the cells were fully charged. Overcharging had to be carried out at a reduced amperage for 4 – 6 hours and it ensured that any weaker cells were brought up to a full charge. It was suggested that, to reduce the charging rate enough, lights should be left on until the desired rate was indicated on the ammeter. The same principle could be used in general operation when the battery was almost charged and the charging rate had therefore to be reduced. The battery terminals should be coated with vaseline or axle grease to prevent them corroding, and the batteries should be housed in a shed which is well-ventilated (though not too exposed as the cells are less efficient at low temperatures), to allow the hydrogen evolved during operation to disperse. For any system, the voltage of the batteries and hence the number of cells will depend on the voltage of the wind generator, and the electrical equipment will have to be adjusted to suit. Provided that the batteries are looked after as suggested, their life will probably exceed that stated by the manufacturers, but if light and power depend upon some time spent on maintenance, then such care will probably be automatic.

Any electrochemical storage system converts chemical energy to electrical energy. A simple torch battery is called a primary cell as, once the chemicals contained within it are exhausted, the electrical current stops and the battery must be replaced with a new one. A conventional accumulator, such as a car battery, is termed a secondary cell as it can be recharged by passing an electric current through it in the reverse direction. A fuel cell also converts chemical energy into electrical energy and will continue to operate as long as it is supplied with chemical energy in the form of fuel and oxidant. The fuel cell can thus be considered as an alternative way of storing power.

A fuel cell is simply another way of converting fuel into electricity. However, unlike the normal fuel-burning heat engine, the fuel cell is not subject to the limitations in efficiency imposed by the Carnot cycle. The most sophisticated fossil-fuel-burning power stations have reached efficiencies of 40 per cent, while the internal-combustion engine is only 10 per cent efficient. However, experimental fuel cells have already obtained efficiencies of 60 − 80 per cent.

The principles of the fuel cell are illustrated by the reaction that occurs when an electric current is passed through impure water. Two electrodes are immersed in water to which acid or alkali has been added to make it conductive. When the electric current is passed, hydrogen is released at the anode and oxygen at the cathode. In a fuel cell the reaction is reversed. Hydrogen is introduced into a negative porous electrode and oxygen into the positive porous electrode. The two re-combine to form water, and an electric current flows between the two electrodes. Many other fuel-cell systems have been developed with differing fuels, electrolytes, electrodes, and temperatures and pressures of operation, all depending upon the final use of the cell. Research is continuing into fuel cells for domestic use powered by natural gas or hydrogen, oxygen/hydrogen cells for space flights and hydrazine-fuelled cells for cars. It might be possible to use one of these systems to provide power storage for wind-generated electricity.

As can be seen from fig. 97, the fuel cell is made of a pair of electrodes between which is trapped a liquid electrolyte. The fuel and oxidant are introduced each on one side of one of the two electrodes, the fuel usually being in gaseous form. The gases are then absorbed into contact with the electrolyte through the porous electrodes, which act as a catalyst for the electrochemical reaction. In practice, a working fuel cell will consist of many cells connected in series to produce a higher output voltage and in parallel to allow a greater current to be drawn from the battery. Many electrodes are clamped together between thin annular spacers, and the fuel or oxidant and electrolyte are circulated alternately in the spaces so formed. The difficulty of obtaining

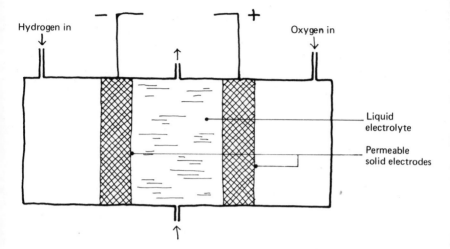

Hydrogen in

Oxygen in

Liquid electrolyte

Permeable solid electrodes

97   Principle of fuel cell operation.

gas, liquid and solid together at the same interface so that the reaction between the ions in the electrolyte and the gas molecules can take place has been a major problem in the development of fuel cells. In practice, each electrode consists of a porous structure either made of or coated with the catalyst. The open pores are closely controlled in size to allow maximum interaction between electrolyte and fuel without allowing the electrolyte to leak through the electrode.

Corrosion too, is a problem with electrodes, and polarization in the cell will also reduce the output voltage so that, when the circuit containing the fuel cell is closed, the voltage is less than the open circuit e.m.f. This voltage drop is caused by the internal resistance of the cell itself, and varies with the current in the circuit; by the inertia of the cell in producing the current, the effect of which inertia is greatest when the cell is producing small currents, and less as the current increases; and by the saturation of the electrode pores with dilute electrolyte, which starves them of the gaseous fuel and oxidant and slows down the reaction. The latter effect is minimal with small currents, but above a given level it increases quickly and eventually sets a limit at which the voltage drops to zero. For this reason the fuel cell has to be designed so that the products of the reaction can be removed from the electrode in order to maintain the efficiency of the cell.

Although research on the fuel cell as defined above has been going on intermittently in both Britain and the USA since Francis Bacon (1969) repeated and extended some of the earlier experiments in electrochemistry made between 1932 and 1938, the first practical application of the fuel cell came in 1962 with the task of developing a

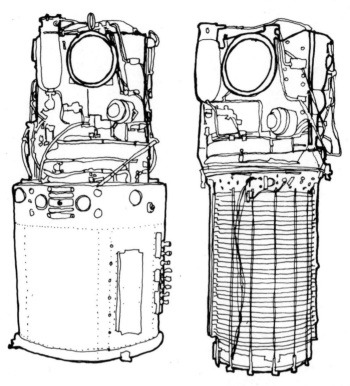

98   *Apollo fuel cell unit (after Bacon, 1969). Each unit stands about 2 ft high.*

hydrogen/oxygen fuel-cell unit for providing auxiliary power in the
Gemini and Apollo space capsules (fig. 98). Because of the restrictions
on weight and the need for a continuous discharge over a three-week
period, conventional batteries would have been unsuitable. The Apollo
battery is made up of 31 cells in series, each cell being about 220 mm
in diameter with electrodes of bi-porous nickel. The electrolyte is 70 –
85 per cent potassium hydroxide, the vapour pressure of the cell being
kept lower than the vapour pressure of the fuel gases. The water
produced during the reaction is evaporated into the hydrogen and
separated from it outside the fuel cell. The fuel cell is rated at 1,420 W
with a maximum capacity of 2,295 W. Three such cells, linked in parallel,
provide all the electricity needed for life support, guidance and
communications during a two-week lunar flight, with an adequate supply
of pure water as a by-product. The hydrogen and oxygen fuels are
carried in the space-craft in a liquid state.

More recently, a use has been found for the fuel cell where a reliable
power source with a reasonably high energy density is needed in a

184

remote situation. The ASEA Co. of Sweden have made a 50-W experimental hydrogen/oxygen fuel battery to power a beacon. A battery of similar type was found to operate without maintenance for six months. Brown-Boveri used a fuel cell to power a television repeater station in the Swiss Alps. The battery used methanol dissolved in the caustic potash electrolyte as a fuel, together with air as the oxidant; it operated for twelve months, after which the electrolyte containing the spent fuel had to be replaced. However, neither system has yet found a real commercial application, chiefly because the cost involved is so much higher than for conventional engine-powered generators.

Following their research into the Apollo fuel cell, Pratt & Whitney have attempted to develop a fuel cell for the domestic market as a means of reducing the expense of energy supply. As gas costs about five times less to distribute than electricity, the idea of 'total energy', with one fuel supplying all power for heating, lighting and running appliances in the house, would simplify this problem. A fuel cell would then be used to convert the incoming gas into the electricity needed. TARGET (Team to Advance Research for Gas Energy) was set up to investigate total energy for housing. An experimental natural-gas fuel cell was developed (see fig. 99) called Powercel 11, which uses natural gas and air as the fuels to produce electricity. First, the methane in the

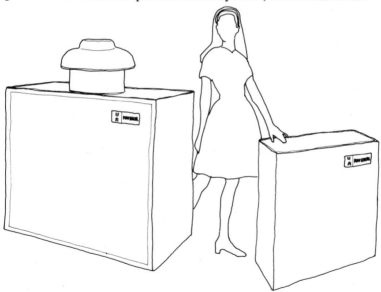

99   Artist's impression of the TARGET Powercel 11 experimental model designed for field tests. A future version is illustrated on the right which will, if the tests are successful, be about a quarter the size and weight of the experimental unit.

natural gas is dissociated in the presence of steam and a catalyst into carbon and hydrogen. The carbon is then oxidized into carbon dioxide, and proceeds with the hydrogen to the fuel cell. This mixture is fed to the anode while air is fed to the cathode, and the hydrogen and oxygen then combine to form water, producing a current in the cell. Each cell produces about 1 V and the total Powercel 11 unit is designed to generate 12½ kW at 120 V and 60 hz, which is 'more than ample to meet the peak electrical needs of the average single-family home' (Orlofsky, 1971). The actual fuel cell is water-cooled, and the heat produced is sufficient to generate the steam required for the reforming process. The power produced is stabilized in an inverter to give the rated output. The early units have operated experimentally with over-all efficiencies of 7 per cent. These experimental units have operated for over 3,200 hours, some of which was in experimental domestic conditions, and although they have been shown to be successful with acceptable pollution and noise levels, 'the major hurdles remaining to achieve a *commercial* system are unit cost and endurance' *(ibid.).*

The fuel cell has also been linked with the 'hydrogen economy', a concept which has arisen as an answer to the diminishing portable fuel resources. Although nuclear power could, in theory, supply unlimited power to the world, once all the detrimental concerns listed earlier were accepted as necessary evils, such power would be produced as electricity or heat and could not supply fuel for transport, etc. However, a nuclear power station could generate electricity which would then be used to electrolyse water to produce hydrogen and oxygen. This would be especially beneficial during off-peak periods, as a nuclear station supplies a continuous load. The hydrogen thus produced could be piped in the same way as gas and used in the home as a fuel for cooking and heating, burning to produce water as a by-product. The hydrogen could also be used in a fuel cell to provide electricity and it has been suggested that tanks of liquid hydrogen could be used to power vehicles, although the safety aspects of this proposition are still being debated.

For autonomous housing, however, the advantages of fuel-cell development would be in the more efficient storage of energy from the wind. As can be seen from fig. 100, wind-produced electricity could be used to electrolyse water into hydrogen and oxygen. The oxygen could then be allowed to escape to the air and the hydrogen stored, as a gas in pressurized tanks, in liquid form under refrigeration, or as a solid metal hydride — the most suitable form of all could such a system be successfully devised. The hydrogen could then be used in a fuel cell, together with oxygen from the air, to provide electricity as and when it was required. The unit could be sized to produce 3 – 4 kW at a maximum although it would probably lie idle or produce a much smaller load for

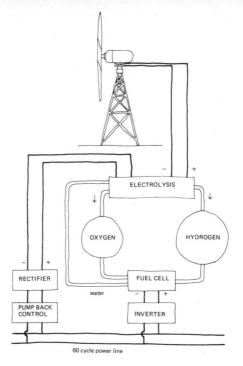

most of the time. Such a wind-energy storage system has been under investigation at Oklahoma State University. The windmill used was a propeller 1.8 m in diameter geared up to a 12 V generator, producing a current of up to 50 amps. This range is good for electrolysis cells, which require low voltage and high current. The electrolyte used was 30 per cent potassium hydroxide, and the gases produced were stored in tanks under pressure. It was then proposed to use the hydrogen produced in a fuel cell, an internal-combustion engine or a simple burner to provide heat or power when required. The system was originally designed for use in under-developed countries and, although performance data are available for the wind-powered electrolysis, no experiments were carried out on re-combining the fuels in a fuel cell.

At first sight, the fuel cell appears a much more attractive power store than batteries. The power could be produced in the right quantities exactly when required. In the cells fuelled with hydrogen (or natural gas) and oxygen (or air), water is a useful by-product, and it might be possible to use the gas from the anaerobic decomposition of organic wastes as the 'methane' input to a reformer. The theoretical efficiencies of such a system are much greater than those obtained by the gas directly in an engine, although the actual efficiencies are probably not so high. However, the two factors of cost and maintenance act against the use of fuel cells, and have probably prevented the development of a commercial unit.

187

The latter factor is probably the more critical. Dr Gregory of the Atomic Energy Research Establishment in Britain has stated that he would not like to have one in his back garden. Compared with a battery, the mechanism and technology involved are considerably more complex, with increased risk of failure. There is also the problem of storing hydrogen under pressure in large tanks near to the house. The dangers of storing petrol, a liquid hydrocarbon fuel, near a house have been widely emphasized. Methane, as previously mentioned, is dangerous if mixed with air, while quantities of hydrogen and air are explosive over a much wider range of concentrations. Great care would therefore be needed when operating the cell to see that the hydrogen and air fuels could not mix and become ignited. Even though TARGET developed a cell that operated automatically, maintenance was one of the problems that has not yet been overcome. The cost of such a cell has also yet to be made competitive. The combined electrode/catalyst often contains materials that are both rare and expensive, such as nickel and platinum. Many promising fuel-cell systems have been experimented with in the laboratory (Bacon, 1969), but so far none appears to have found a commercial potential which would make the cost competitive with conventional gas-powered generators or secondary storage batteries.

Having failed to find a solution to power storage in fuel cells, which prove aesthetically pleasing but are very complex to realize, electric power storage in batteries is by far the cheapest. Even so, the battery cost can be equal to the wind generator cost, proportionately increasing the cost of the 'free' wind energy. At present, the only way to reduce and simplify the cost of power storage is to use less power and restrict its use to essential, high-efficiency equipment.

Table 15 Cost of fuel for fuel cells. Costs given are those for 1966 relative to the cost of hydrazine, which is taken as 100.

Fuel	Relative cost in bulk	Efficiency of oxidation (%)	Relative fuel costs/Kwh
Hydrogen	100	60	8.5
*Hydrazine hydrate	100	60	100
Methanol	6.4	50	3.4
Ammonia	14.3	25	4.5
Propane	6.4	20	4.0
Town gas	2.3	20	2.5
Sodium	22.9	60	90

* Only the hydrogen liberated from the hydrazine hydrate is usable as fuel in the fuel cell.

(Original data taken from A.I. Harrison and G.R. Lomax, 'Applications and costs of electrical energy sources' in D.H. Collins (ed.), Power Sources 1966, Pergamon Press, Oxford)

8 Storing heat

If the sun shone continuously, then it would be possible to construct some form of shelter that would always provide an adequate indoor temperature. Entering a greenhouse on a cold but sunny winter's day will often bring a pleasant surprise when the warmth of the air inside is appreciated. However, more skill is needed to maintain the temperature of the shelter at night, and also during periods of overcast weather, unless some auxiliary method of heating is used. This is not necessarily a bad system: a house designed to provide solar heating on sunny days, if built so that the large glass areas needed for this purpose could be covered with insulation when the sun was not shining, could be adequately heated by burning a reduced amount of fossil fuel, and would thus demonstrate an over-all fuel saving.

Previously, however, and for the purposes of the map on p. 32, a solar-heated house has been defined as a building that contains some method of storing the solar energy for use during times when the sun is not shining. This can be done in three different ways. Solar energy can be stored as heat from summer to winter, the solar radiation being collected when it is most plentiful with the collectors operating at higher temperatures. Alternatively, the collection system can be designed to operate at winter temperatures, with the excess heat produced on sunny days stored over a short term for use during periods of overcast weather. Lastly, where the winter climate is cold but sunny, the solar energy can be collected during the day and stored for heating the house during the evening. Generally, however, these last two methods of storage are less well-defined, the length of time that the heat is stored depending on the amount of solar radiation received during the particular day and the demand for heat made by the house, which in turn depends upon the outside temperature.

Seasonal heat storage has advantages and disadvantages. It is possible in the more northerly latitudes of Britain and Canada (Alcutt and Hooper, 1961) to collect sufficient solar energy in summer to meet the heating demand of a house throughout the winter, whereas in winter very high levels of insulation and low ventilation rates are required

189

before it is possible to balance the incoming radiation which can be collected against the heat that is required. However, such a storage system necessitates a large volume of some material, usually water or rock, to store the heat, and this, together with its necessary container and insulation, has until now made this method prohibitively expensive. Not only is the storage medium expensive, but space must be provided for it within the building, logically in an insulated basement, and this again increases the initial cost of construction. As the collectors will operate at much higher temperatures in summer, the storage will be heated to a corresponding level. Although higher storage temperatures mean that the total volume of storage can be reduced, the collector will operate at much lower temperatures in winter, and this heat will be unsuitable for topping up the stored heat. Putting warmed water into a tank of water at a much higher temperature will have the effect of lowering the overall temperature. Thus either the collector can only operate in summer or, in order to reduce the volume for seasonal heat storage, an alternative winter storage must be used at a lower temperature, backed up by the stored summer heat. This doubling of equipment increases the cost of the system, and also means that part of the house is occupied by a storage bin which is of no practical use for half the year. For all these reasons, very few attempts have been made to build long-term heat stores, although the scarcity and increasing costs of fuel may readjust the economic position of long-term collection.

Most work has been directed towards determining the economic storage volume, allowing for the use of auxiliary heating. In a system of this kind the collector continues to operate during the winter, and the heat collected is not only used directly in the building, but also stored at lower temperatures when there is an excess. Even though the storage temperature is lower, it is still sufficient for warm-air or low-temperature radiant water heating. The task is now to evaluate the cost of the storage needed to supply all the heat required for the longest period of overcast weather that might possibly occur, and to set this against the cost of supplying auxiliary energy during this period. Such an evaluation is meaningless unless there is sufficient solar energy to collect and store for these purposes. In Britain this is probably not the case, except where a much-reduced heating demand could be established.

For normal houses in the USA, however, where more southerly latitudes give higher levels of incident solar radiation, it may be possible to construct total solar heating systems with adequate storage capacity. Thomason (1969), with a large storage volume of water and stones, could supply heat to his house in Washington for 5 – 10 consecutive overcast days, and had thus constructed a house-heating system operating almost entirely by the solar method, provided that all the components were operating efficiently. However, the MIT III house provided only two days' supply of heat from storage, and that only if the storage water was at its maximum design temperature at the start of the two days. The house had a back-up system consisting of an immersion heater in the hot-water storage tank. This system was an attempt to balance the cost of the storage against the cost of the extra electricity needed during cold, cloudy spells. Such a system would need most auxiliary heating during the coldest months of December, January and February but with the higher outside temperatures of the other winter months and the consequently reduced heating demand in the house, the storage would probably be capable of supplying heat for a longer period of cloudy weather. In Britain the storage problem is less one of evaluating the cost of auxiliary energy, as there would probably be insufficient area on a normal house to collect enough sunshine during the winter. Auxiliary heating then becomes a necessity to maintain comfortable conditions, unless long-term seasonal heat storage is used.

At the climatic extreme of a desert condition, as in the south-west of the USA, where cold, sunny days occur almost continuously throughout the winter, it may be sufficient to use a very small volume of storage. This would be just large enough to store solar energy collected during the day to heat the building at night. Small amounts of auxiliary heat would then be used for overcast days. Most systems of this type combine the collecting and storage materials in a single component which forms part of the building fabric.

The material used for heat storage has, in nearly every case, been water or rock or some combination of the two. However, attempts have been made to find materials that will store more heat in a smaller volume by the action of the heat initiating a phase change or chemical reaction in them. However, in any evaluation of the materials used for storing heat, other criteria must also be considered. These include the cost of the heat-storage medium, the cost of containers for it, the cost and ease of insulating the heat store, the method of transferring heat from the collector to storage and from the storage to the building, and of course the efficiency of the material as a heat-storage medium.

Considering all these points, water proves to be the best method found to date of storing heat. Water has a specific heat of 1 cal/gm/deg C and will therefore store more heat per unit volume than rocks or sand. It is a cheap material to provide, and fits logically into a solar heating system where water is the heat-transfer fluid in the collector, and low-temperature radiant ceiling panels are used in the rooms. Nevertheless, the containers for water are relatively expensive, especially where tanks of large volume are required. When the solar-heated water is fed into the storage tank, convection currents are set up and the temperature of the tank soon becomes uniform. Convection currents also increase the heat loss from the tank, unless it is well insulated, but they can be avoided by stratifying the heat within the tank. The heated water is fed into the top of the tank, and cold water for heating in the collector is withdrawn from the bottom. Baffles placed in the tank will also interrupt the convection currents.

A rock or pebble storage bed will store less heat per unit volume than water (see table 16) as not only is the specific heat of rock lower, but voids are left between the rocks. In an ideal situation the voids might occupy 30 per cent of the total volume, although this is more likely to be 40 per cent or more in practice. However, the air path formed between the rocks is very tortuous, and when air is blown through the pebble storage bed the surface area for the heat exchange is large. Rocks and pebbles, like water, are cheap, and they are suited to a system where air is being heated in a solar collector and warm air is used to distribute the heat to the rooms. Unlike water, the rocks only touch at points, and hence the heat is not distributed evenly throughout the bed. This is an advantage as the hot air will warm up a portion of the heat storage bed immediately where it enters it, the air leaving the bed being at the temperature of the cool end (see fig. 101). As the sun continues to shine, more of the bed is heated to a higher temperature. If, however, only a small portion of the bed has been heated, air from the rooms can be blown through the rock store and heated to the higher temperature. Unlike that of water, the capacity of a rock storage bed can vary exactly with the amount of heat available to put in it. Containers must also be provided for the rocks but these can be much cheaper as they do not have to be watertight. Nevertheless, air leakage is often a problem in an air solar heating system because of pressure differences within the system. The space occupied in a house by a rock storage bed will be greater than the volume of a water storage system of equivalent capacity.

Table 16 Sensible heat storage capacity of some common materials

Material	Specific heat kcal/kg/deg C	Density kg/m^3	Unit heat capacity kcal/m^3/deg C		
			No voids	30% voids	40% voids
Water	1.0	1000	1000	(1000)	(1000)
Scrap iron	0.11	7848	881	609	529
Magnetite	0.17	5125	849	593	513
Scrap aluminium	0.22	2720	577	400	352
Concrete	0.27	2242	609	416	368
Rock	0.21	2883	593	416	352
Brick	0.20	2242	449	320	272

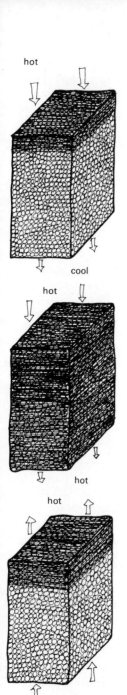

hot

cool

Heating the bed
As the hot air enters the bed the pebbles at the top are heated immediately. The air leaving the bed however is still at the initial temperature of the rock. As the heating continues the dark band representing the hot/cold boundary between the pebbles moves down the bed.

hot

hot

Heating the bed
Only when the dark band has moved right to the base of the bed and the entire bed has been filled with heat does the temperature of the air leaving the bottom begin to rise.

hot

cool

Heating the house
The cool air from the house enters at the base of the bed. It leaves the bed at a temperature nearly equal to the temperature of the pebbles at the top i.e. almost the same temperature as that of the hot air entering during the heating part of the cycle. Therefore even when the bed is only half full of heat air delivered from it is mostly at the highest temperature of the operational cycle.

101   Heat storage in a pebble bed.

193

Table 16 shows heat storage values for other materials, such as scrap metal, which might also be used. Although the density of metals is high, so that they store more heat for a unit volume of material than rock, they still have the disadvantages of rock when compared with water and are generally much more expensive.

The other method of heat storage which has been given considerable attention is the use of chemicals which absorb heat to produce a change of state. The heat is regenerated when the process is reversed. Chemical heat storage methods were developed to reduce the total volume of storage needed and hence the amount of floor space occupied by the storage in the house. For such a system a chemical is required which changes phase at a temperature corresponding to the temperatures generated in a solar collector. The two chemicals most studied in this respect are sodium sulphate $Na_2SO_4.10H_2O$ (Glauber's salts) and sodium phosphate dodecahydrate $Na_2HPO_4.12H_2O$. The former melts at about 33° C, absorbing 58 kcal/kg to change the solid into the liquid, while sodium phosphate melts at 36° C, absorbing 63 kcal/kg. If Glauber's salts are used as the heat storage medium, air or water heated above 33° C in a solar collector and circulated through the salts will cause them to melt and, in so doing, absorb heat. When the salts are in the liquid phase and air or water for house heating at temperatures below 32° C is circulated through the heat storage medium, the salts recrystallize and give up the heat of recrystallization to the air or water. Because of the nature of the chemical change involved, after repeated heating and cooling cycles the salts fail to absorb and give up the full theoretical value of the heat involved and the capacity of the storage drops. In the Dover house, which had a collector area of 69 m^2 and a total storage volume of 13 m^3 (about 21 T of Glauber's salts), the theoretical capacity of the storage was computed to be sufficient for twelve days' normal winter heating requirements. Although the collector and storage system were adequate to provide all the heating necessary over the first winter, auxiliary heat had to be used in later, colder winters as the chemical storage capacity decreased.

Because of the attention paid to chemical storage and its advantages over conventional water and rock storage systems which can only store sensible heat, some explanation of the mechanism and failure of these systems is justified. At 33° C, hydrated sodium sulphate changes into the anhydrous salt and water. Some of the anhydrous salt then dissolves in the water released to form a saturated solution, the water formed as the salts decompose being only sufficient to dissolve about half the anhydrous salt formed. The undissolved salts settle out at the bottom of the container. As the saturated solution cools, only the anhydrous sodium sulphate in immediate contact with the water, that is the portion dissolved in it, can recombine immediately with the water of crystallization. Unless the mixture is stirred to bring all the anhydrous salt in contact with the water, only half the heat will be regenerated. Apart from stirring, attempts to relieve the problem of stratification of the water and the anhydrous salt have been concerned with the design of the containers. Shallow pans which provide a much larger area of contact between the water and the anhydrous salt also increase the surface area and cost of the container. Otherwise, ways have been sought of maintaining the anhydrous salt in small batches in some form of matrix within the saturated solution.

Another problem with the phase-change method of storing heat is the phenomenon of super-cooling. A saturated solution of anhydrous salt and water can, if undisturbed, cool below the temperature at which the two recombine. At some point below this temperature the two will recombine and the temperature of the solution will rise with the expected evolution of heat. However, this can be a problem when used for house heating, as circulating the cool house air around the salts may not be sufficient to make the salts solidify. Recrystallization can be induced by seeding the saturated solution with a suitable agent but this again adds to the problems of the design and use of the system. The tendency to super-cool appears to be random, whereas the increasing number of heating and cooling cycles is known to decrease the storage capacity through stratification.

Although many phase-change and chemical-change systems involving such factors as heats of melting, heats of solution, heats of vaporization and chemical reaction in solution, have been cited (Goldstein, 1969) as having potential for the storage of heat, most of them exhibit engineering problems when applied to solar heating systems. Such would be the case with the vapour-absorption method of heat storage. This involves the heat taken up when a liquid changes to a vapour. However, because so much more vapour than liquid is produced (1 litre of water, boiled away, produces 1,700 litres of steam), another medium is used to absorb this vapour. For example, if a concentrated solution of sulphuric acid and water is heated sufficiently, the water will be distilled out and can be condensed as a liquid in the cooler part of the system, circulating air or water being used for cooling. When the sulphuric acid with its remaining residue of water is later cooled, the vapour pressure in this half of the system drops and water from the cooler part of the system evaporates to equalize the pressure. On returning to the very concentrated solution of sulphuric acid the water gives up its heat of condensation, together with the heat of mixing with the sulphuric acid. A valve can be introduced to isolate the two chambers, and the heat can then be stored until required (see fig. 102). Although the heat (530 kcal/kg) involved

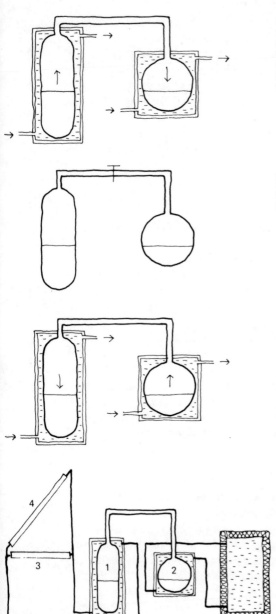

Water heated by solar energy is circulated through a water jacket surrounding a vessel containing a solution of sulphuric acid and water. The water boils off and condenses in another vessel with a cold water jacket. The first vessel now contains concentrated sulphuric acid.

At the end of the charging period a valve between the two vessels is closed and the apparatus cools down. As it cools the pressure in the acid container drops.

When heat is required the valve is opened. As the pressure in the acid container is lower than that in the water container the water evaporates and mixes with the concentrated acid. When this happens heat is evolved which can be transferred to the surrounding water and used for space heating.

A hypothetical solar heating system: water from a solar collector (4) is circulated round a vessel (1) containing a solution of sulphuric acid and water. Water from an insulated tank is circulated round vessel (2) where the pure water from (1) condenses. As the water condenses heat is given up to the circulating water. When the sun stops shining the collector connections are shut off and vessel (1) cools. Water from the insulated tank is circulated round vessel (2) to maintain the highest possible temperature difference between (1) and (2). When space heating is required the water surrounding (1) can be circulated through a radiant ceiling panel (3). The evaporation of water in (2) cools the surrounding water which can then be used when the system is charging.

102 *A theoretical two-vessel chemical heat storage system.*

196

as the water changes from vapour to liquid is of a greater magnitude than for the phase-change from solid to liquid, the system, although simple in theory, would probably present many difficulties if constructed. For this reason, salts and eutectic mixtures which have suitable melting-points and change from solid to liquid seem the most appropriate for house heating, but even the systems tried have shown that the problems of stratification and super-cooling reduce the effective storage capacity over a period of time. Most of the chemical systems are potentially corrosive and are also more expensive than water or rock. The University of Pennsylvania (1972) did some work on the use of phase-change materials for thermal storage in air-conditioning systems. After failing to prevent stratification in hydrated salt systems for more than ten freezing/thawing cycles, they surveyed the salt hydrates available but could find none with a high heat of fusion, a suitable melting-point and a low cost. Their only positive suggestion was the use of organic waxes melting at a suitable temperature for heat storage, but here again costs would be high and the waxes might also be viewed as a fire hazard.

Whether it is worth the effort to find some new wonder material for the storage of heat is questionable. The only economic advantage in such a discovery would be a decrease in the volume occupied by the storage. Baer (1973) has demonstrated in practice that the volume of storage can be reduced by using the storage material itself, in this case oil drums filled with water, as the building material for the wall. The consideration at the design stage of a building of putting in a basement or semi-basement for rock storage might provide a cheaper alternative to the use of chemicals, which, although intellectually sophisticated, has so far been shown to have serious drawbacks when applied in practice.

The only building so far purposely constructed to collect and store heat from summer to winter was the first house built at the Massachusetts Institute of Technology in 1939, designed in part to develop systems for estimating the performance of flat-plate solar collectors. The two-roomed laboratory had a collector of blackened copper tubes soldered to a copper sheet mounted on the south-facing roof. The area of the collector was just over 33 m^2. The building sat over a basement which contained a 67,500-litre hot-water storage tank surrounded by insulation. Heat was collected during the summer and stored for use in the winter. The building operated for two seasons without any auxiliary heating. As can be seen from the graph, the water in summer was heated to about 91° C. This meant that no further heat could be collected over the beginning of the winter, as the temperature of the collector would be lower than in summer. Only in the middle of February, when the temperature of the storage tank had dropped to 54° C, could heat from the collector usefully be put into the system.

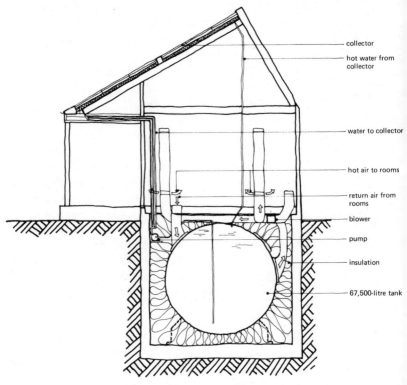

103   MIT solar house 1 (after Hottel and Cabot, 1955).

The heat from storage was distributed to the house by a warm-air system, air being blown around the surface of the tank. At the time, the system was thought to be very uneconomic, but it did demonstrate that long-term storage was possible in the east of the USA. Since much thought has been given to the optimum volume of storage per unit area of collector, using either water or rock, it is useful to note that the first solar house at MIT had a storage-to-collector ratio of approximately 2,020 litre/m^2 of collector area.

If the total energy that can be collected from a given area in winter is equal to the energy required to heat the house, then it should theoretically be possible to provide a solar heating system for the house. In assessing the volume of storage needed for such a system, the data for the coldest and least sunny month must be used. The storage will then supply heat during the longest period of overcast weather, the system being over-designed for the remaining months in the heating season. Thomason attempted to achieve this degree of total winter solar heating in his first house in Washington. In fact the system provided about 95 per cent of the heat requirements of the house, a supplementary 123 litres of oil being necessary for the first winter and 167 litres for the second winter of operation. The collector had an area of 78 m^2, while the compound storage consisted of a 6,350-litre hot-water drum and a 1,090-litre tank which acted as a domestic hot-water pre-heater, the whole being surrounded by 44 T of rock. The hot water from the collector passed through the domestic water tank to the main hot-water storage tank. The heat then passed to the stones and from there to the rooms (see fig. 105).

Because the domestic hot water was heated partly by the sun, taking heat both directly from the collector and also from storage, it is difficult to give an accurate storage-to-collector ratio for the Thomason house. However, as the same collector was used for both domestic water heating and space heating, it seems reasonable to take a total ratio for the whole system. The heat capacity of the rock can be estimated as the equivalent if the heat were to be stored in water. This gives a total storage capacity of 16,240 litres which means a storage-to-collector ratio of approximately 210 litre/m^2. The storage was initially heated to 52° C, and Thomason

104   *Hot-water storage tank temperatures in MIT 1 (after Hottel and Cabot, 1955).*

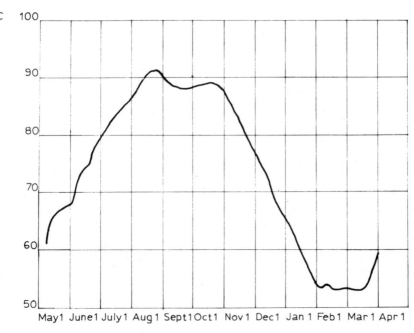

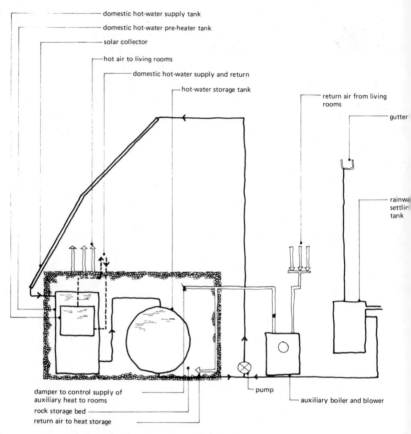

domestic hot-water supply tank

domestic hot-water pre-heater tank

solar collector

hot air to living rooms

domestic hot-water supply and return

hot-water storage tank

return air from living rooms

gutter

rainwa
settlin
tank

damper to control supply of auxiliary heat to rooms

pump

rock storage bed

auxiliary boiler and blower

return air to heat storage

105   Collection and storage system in the first Thomason house, Washington, D.C. (after Thomason, 1961). The water-heating collector is integrated into the roof of the house and storage is accomplished in the 6,350-litre tank surrounded by 44T of small rocks housed in the basement. The heat from the solar-heated water in the tank passes into the stones so that the water is cooled ready to absorb more heat in the collector. Air from the rooms is blown through the rocks until it warms to 22°C–24°C, when it passes to the house. The warm water from the collector is also used to indirectly heat the domestic hot-water supply. The solar heating system provided 95% of the space-heating demand during the first winter of operation, together with most of the hot-water heating. The designed storage capacity was 5 days. The collector was turned 10° west of south to take advantage of the clear afternoon sunshine in winter. However, the system could also be used for summer cooling by pumping the water through the collector at night so that the heat radiated to the sky. The water would then cool down the storage bed so that air could be blown through it during the day and supplied cool to the house. The rainwater was used to top up any water lost by evaporation in the collector.

estimated that the heat thus stored should be sufficient to keep the house at about 21° C for five or more cold cloudy days with outside temperatures of −4° C to + 7° C. If the house were only heated to 16° C, then this storage period could be extended to cover 7 − 10 days of cloudy weather. When the stored heat was eventually exhausted, the temperature of the storage was found to have dropped to 18 ° C at the bottom of the heat storage bin and 24° C at the top.

However, as the cost of auxiliary fuel was not high at that time it could be argued that this amount of storage was not economic, even though almost total solar heating was achieved. In an autonomous house 95 per cent solar heating might be thought adequate, with the low temperatures on some days being suffered without auxiliary heating. In an effort to be economic, the MIT IV house was designed to gain only 75 per cent of its winter heat from the sun. This target figure was reduced to an average 50 per cent in practice. The house had a total collection area of 59 m^2 and a hot-water storage tank of 5,955 litres, giving a storage:collection ratio of about 100 litre/m^2. The reduced collector area and storage volume were supplemented by an auxiliary oil-fired boiler.

The problem was later analysed in detail in order to find the exact economic size of collector and storage. Anderson, Hottel and Whillier (1955) devised a method for analysing the volume of sensible-heat storage using empirical data. For a given locality it predicts the fraction F of the total energy requirements that must be provided over a fixed period by auxiliary fuel, given a solar collector of area A and a heat storage capacity of B kcal/degC/m^2 of collector. The graph gives the analysis for Blue Hill, Massachusetts, showing that if some storage is provided, however small the amount, then the fractional auxiliary energy requirement is decreased. More important, the data illustrated by the graph indicate that as the storage capacity increases above 146 kcal/deg C/m^2, i.e. more than 146 litres of water per square metre of collector, then the reduction in the amount of auxiliary energy required becomes progressively less. For complete solar heating, the collector would have to be so sized that the average energy requirement was about 70 per cent of the total amount that could be collected, provided that the storage capacity was about 117/kcal/deg C/m^2 or more. This would entail a large, expensive collector. Alternatively, the fractional auxiliary requirement can be reduced by making the storage capacity, i.e. the total storage volume, as large as possible, so that the average energy requirement approaches the average useful collection of energy and the size of the collector is thus reduced. Because of the optimization around a storage capacity of 97 − 146 litres of water per square metre of collector, this value has been used as a guide for many designs.

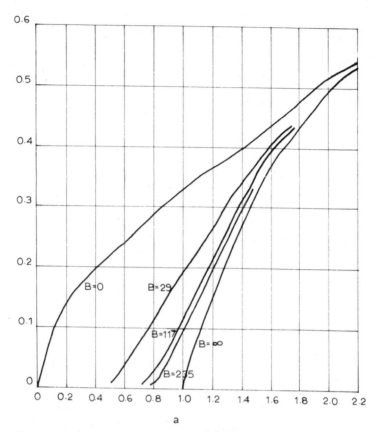

106 *Graph relating auxiliary energy requirements to heat collection and storage, based on six years' experimental data (after Anderson, Hottel and Whillier, 1955).*
F = *auxiliary requirement/total requirement*
a = *average energy requirement/average useful collection*
Average horizontal solar incidence for the site = 71 W/m²
*Average useful collection (collector covered with two glass plates tilted at 55°
to horizontal at a temperature 10°C above ambient temperature) = 64 W/m²*
B = *capacity of storage system in kcal/deg C/m² of collector*

However, the cost basis on which this study was based has not necessarily remained the same. Moreover, the cost of additional collector area is probably higher than the cost of additional storage. Speyer (1969) stated that, because storage costs represent the smaller part of the total cost of a solar heating system (working from 1959 prices for the USA), storage costs would have to be reduced by 80 per cent before solar heating became competitive. He also estimated that if collector costs could be reduced by a factor of 2 or 3, then solar heating could become competitive. This would suggest that the cheap collector was a better goal to aim for than increased efficiency of storage. Increased efficiency of storage could mean storing heat at a higher temperature, but this would directly affect the process of collection, as the efficiency of collection drops with increasing temperature.

Buchberg and Roulet (1968) also appear to find collector costs the limiting parameter in their optimization of solar collection and storage systems. For defined optima of collector area and storage, a target cost for the collector was established. Thus, with a collector area of 39 m^2 and a storage volume of 1,290 litres, once the cost of auxiliary heating, storage insulation and piping had been taken into consideration, the collector cost has to be less than $11/m^2. As the collector and storage increased in size to take a larger percentage of the total house heating, so the target cost for the collector decreased below a possible limit. They concluded that only short-term storage was viable, and suggested that the economic situation might be improved if the collector were integrated into the roof structure and if it were also used for summer water heating and space cooling.

In a similar way, Tybout and Löf (1970) studied the value of solar heating with regard to collector area and storage capacity. They concluded that nowhere in America was 100 per cent solar heating economic, although this conclusion was based only on the value of the fuel which the free solar energy replaced. Thus an auxiliary heating system, which cost about the same as a normal heating system, was provided, the cost of supplying the solar energy being offset only against the value of the conventional fuel thus saved. For partial solar heating they found that, for the cost of the system to be at a minimum, the storage volume should be reduced to $49 - 75$ litre/m^2 of collector, which gives an equivalent of $1 - 2$ days' average winter heating requirement in America.

All these attempts at optimization may not be as relevant where autonomy is sought. Granted that there will be no auxiliary heating, the storage must be of a size to supply heat for the coldest months of January and December. The system will be oversized for the remaining winter months. The cost of the auxiliary system can then be set against the necessary costs of collector and storage. However, although storage can be provided at a relatively small extra cost, it is the limit in area which becomes important in designing the system, rather than the costs of collector or storage. It may be physically impossible to provide sufficient surface area on the building to meet the maximum demand in midwinter. However well the building is insulated, there must be a point at which the heat gain from the collecting surfaces balances the heat loss from the non-collecting surfaces. At what climatic conditions this limit can be reached has not been established but it seems unlikely that the balance can be achieved in midwinter in Britain. It might therefore be possible to design the system and storage to provide total solar heating for the months at the beginning and end of the winter, with some other heating used for the colder months. This might take the form of long-term high-temperature storage, whereby a volume of water is heated up in summer and the heat used for space heating in December and January only. Provision of this additional storage would, of course, mean extra expense. Alternatively, a regenerative fuel such as wood might be grown on site for use during the colder months. Such a solar collection and storage system would not be optimized in the terms discussed previously but, nevertheless, total autonomous space heating could be achieved.

Diurnal variations in temperature are significant when the fabric of the building is considered. Any heating within a building not only contributes to the comfort of the occupants but also raises the temperature of the surrounding walls, ceiling and floor. If the internal temperature falls, for instance when the heating is switched off at night, then the heat flows from the fabric of the building to the colder inside air. The materials of which the walls, ceiling and floor are made can therefore act as a heat store. At St George's School, Wallasey (see p.42), where the building was constructed of mass materials well insulated on the outside to lower the transfer of heat from inside to outside, the ceiling temperature rose by just over 1.5° C on a sunny winter's day but remained virtually constant on an overcast winter's day. On both days, however, the temperature was about 18° C, despite the fact that on the sunny day the heat input to the building was $117\ W/m^2$ of window area, while on the preceding overcast day it was $69\ W/m^2$.

The comment sometimes made in relation to traditional methods of construction, to the effect that thick earth walls are warm in winter and cool in summer, is not strictly true, as it seems probable that the wall temperatures remain relatively constant throughout the year, rising only slightly in summer; it is the external air temperature that actually varies. The recent development and use of light-framed buildings has led to a change in the heating pattern. A well-insulated lightweight building will heat up quickly, as little heat is needed to raise the surface temperature of the walls. As soon as the heating is switched off, the building cools down, the heat flowing through the walls to the cold outside. This means that heat is only put into the building when it is required. For an autonomous house, where heat is not always available, some thermal mass is necessary to even out the temperatures during periods of cloudy weather when no solar heat can be collected. To conserve energy, it might also be necessary to provide internal insulated surfaces which will warm up quickly when the room is occupied. Smith (1973) suggests therefore that massive walls may not be necessary and a light-framed insulated structure may be a more efficient user of the solar heat in that extra energy is not required for warming the building fabric, the thermal mass being provided by the heat store itself.

However, the choice of building fabric may also be influenced by the materials available and the money to be spent. Thus, if on-site materials are chosen to complement on-site energy sources, earth walls may be the best choice. If these are then insulated on the outside, the fabric of the building will have a low heat-transfer characteristic and will also act as a good heat store.

Any heat stored in the fabric of the building will be at relatively low temperatures and will in fact provide only a background tempering of the internal environment. For a solar heating system, the temperature of the storage must be a compromise between efficiency of collection, efficiency of storing and the level of comfort within the building. For high efficiency of collection, low temperatures are required, whereas for a small storage volume of given capacity higher temperatures would be convenient. These would also make for more comfortable conditions within the house. It has often been suggested that solar energy might be collected more efficiently at lower temperatures, and then upgraded with a heat pump to a level more suitable for home heating. Any such use would have no real effect on the volume of heat storage needed since, although the storing of energy at lower temperatures would apparently necessitate a greater volume, this would in turn be reduced by the fact that collection could take place at lower insolation levels. Thus the Bliss solar-heated laboratory at Tucson (p.103), which used a heat pump in the system, had a collector area of 150 m^2, a storage tank of 17,870 litres and a storage-to-collector ratio of about 120 litre/m^2, which is about the same as the value recommended by Whillier et al. and that used at MIT IV.

One other method of storing solar energy for space heating has been suggested, namely that of converting the direct solar energy to mechanical energy which can then be converted and stored as potential energy. This principle has been used in the U.K. by the Central Electricity Generating Board. Off-peak electricity is used to pump water to an upper reservoir. During peak periods, water can be run out from this reservoir through turbines to boost the supply of electricity. A similar idea was used in a mine in New Mexico where a solar engine pumped water to a store in the daytime. This water was then run through a dynamo, and provided electricity to light the mine by day and night. However, such a method of storage is really only applicable on a large scale as, to store appreciable quantities of energy, either large volumes of water or large heights must be involved. Daniels (1964) estimates that the storing of 1 kWh of energy in a reservoir 1 m above pumping level would require the lifting and storing of 367,000 litres of water, which is far beyond the scale of a single house. At the same time, the conversion of the direct solar energy to mechanical energy for pumping is inefficient, and mechanical storage of solar energy therefore seems inapplicable to the problem of autonomous housing.

Apart from other limitations of the heat store, it is essential to maintain the temperature of the stored heat until it is required, which means that some insulation of the store is needed. The provision of insulation increases the cost of the solar system proportionally to the volume of storage used, while the actual amount of insulation used depends on the temperature at which the heat is stored. For seasonal heat storage, insulation is very important; for example, a mass of water at 50° C in a tank insulated with 300 mm of expanded polystyrene will only suffer a 5 deg C drop in temperature over a period of a month. For short-term storage the insulation thickness can be smaller, and placing the storage within the framework of the house will ensure that any heat lost is gained by the building. However, where heat is stored under the house, whether in rock, sand or water, the storage should probably be separated from the surrounding earth by insulation. Although heat could theoretically be stored in the ground and recovered just as in any regular rock or sand storage bed, any movements of water within the soil would increase the heat loss from storage. Thus, unless ground-water patterns are known, it is probably better to rely on some independent heat store rather than on the earth directly beneath the house.

In northern latitudes some form of heat storage is needed with any solar heating system, and even in climates where winter insolation levels are higher, as in south-west America, enough heat storage must be provided to warm the house during the evening and night. This reduced need for storage has encouraged the development of passive collectors in which the body of water or rock forms both the collector and the heat store, with movable insulation to reduce the heat loss from the storage to the outside at night. These principles are used in the Baer solar-heated zome, Hay's Solarchitecture house in California, and the solar wall of Trombe and Michel in the Pyrenees (see pp. 44–6).

Of the materials used for the more conventional type of heat storage, water is the most suitable as it is cheap, has a high heat capacity, can be used as the heat transfer medium in the collector and, if the storage is arranged in the right relation to the collector system, can be made to thermosiphon, thus saving the energy needed for at least one pump.

However, the use of sand or rock as a heat storage medium has the advantage that the containers required are much simpler. A blower must be used to reclaim the heat from the rock, however, which necessitates extra energy. If hot-air heating is used within the house, a blower will have to be provided anyway, and the two systems might be combined. Either method of sensible-heat storage will be cheaper than using a phase-change material. Even though, without any further development in chemical storage systems, a salt hydrate storage system would take up only 20 per cent of the volume of a water tank of equivalent storage capacity, the cost of the chemical system would be three times that of a pumped water storage system (Dudley, 1972). The salt hydrate systems also involve problems of corrosion, and for these reasons the simple sensible-heat storage methods seem preferable. This is borne out by the examples of solar-heated houses discussed earlier, most of which use some method of sensible-heat storage. The one advantage of salt hydrate systems, namely a reduction in the total volume of storage, may even prove to be a disadvantage. A brick wall with additional insulation might cost more than a light-framed, well-insulated construction of equivalent U-value. Assuming that some mass is needed to temper the internal environment of the house, this mass could more easily be provided by the large volume of water or rock storage with a cheaper external wall construction than by more expensive massive walls with a more expensive, higher-capacity storage of smaller mass.

In order to achieve full autonomy, economic optimization of storage may have to be replaced, especially in more northerly latitudes, by the provision of different types of storage at varying temperatures to make full use of the income energy available for space heating, even though the capital cost is thereby raised.

For the autonomous house, however, cost may be a misleading parameter. Whether it be for heat storage, power generation or any of the other aspects discussed, a higher capital cost becomes tolerable if the choice is between economy and survival.

Appendix: a design for an autonomous house

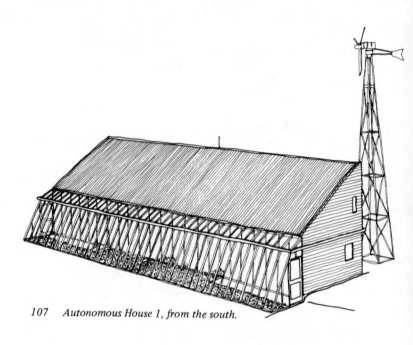

107   Autonomous House 1, from the south.

The data assembled in the book have been used as the basis for the design of an autonomous house for a family of four, sited on a one-acre plot. The house is a highly insulated structure, in terms both of the skin of the building and of the ventilation rate, which is low, in order to reduce the heating demand to a minimum. The form of the house results from the need to have a large south-facing surface, while at the same time permitting sunshine to enter the rooms. The water-heating solar collector on the roof cannot by its nature be transparent, but the long south-facing conservatory provides a source of solar-heated air for space heating and allows sunlight into the rooms; it also acts as an indoor garden. The north-facing side of the house has few windows, to lessen the heat loss. The 'attics' upstairs are designed to be mainly closed off in winter with insulated shutters to save on heating. Apart from heating the domestic hot water, the collector provides a surplus of heat which contributes to the heating of the house. Any surplus electricity produced by the 2 kW windmill, after the requirements for lighting, refrigerator, radio, iron and pumps and fans for the heating system have been met, passes through heating coils in the earth heat storage battery under the house. Rainwater is collected and purified for drinking and waste washing water is purified and re-used. The heat contained in the waste washing water is used to heat the methane digester. The digestion of the manure produced by the stock and the vegetable waste from the holding and the human sewage produces enough gas for cooking. The house was costed in 1972 at the same price per square metre as a traditional brick-built house.

A house based on this design is planned to be built on the campus at Brunel University, Uxbridge, Middlesex. The house will be used as student accommodation and will be on a site of approximately 0.8 ha.

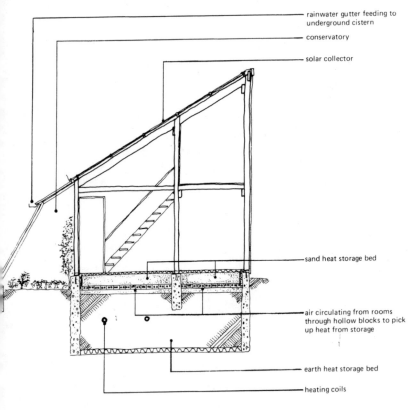

rainwater gutter feeding to underground cistern

conservatory

solar collector

sand heat storage bed

air circulating from rooms through hollow blocks to pick up heat from storage

earth heat storage bed

heating coils

108   Section through house.

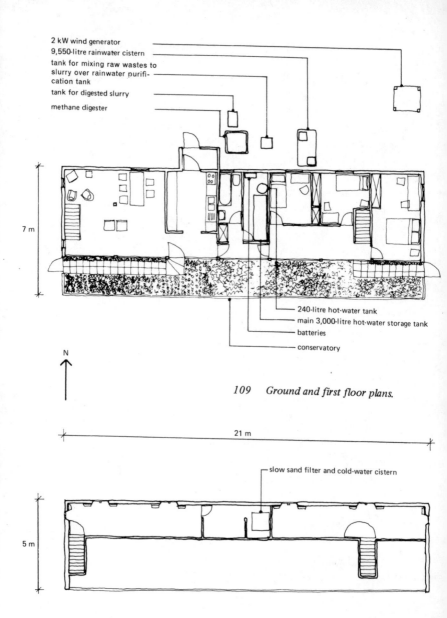

2 kW wind generator
9,550-litre rainwater cistern
tank for mixing raw wastes to slurry over rainwater purification tank
tank for digested slurry
methane digester

7 m

240-litre hot-water tank
main 3,000-litre hot-water storage tank
batteries
conservatory

N

109   Ground and first floor plans.

21 m

slow sand filter and cold-water cistern

5 m

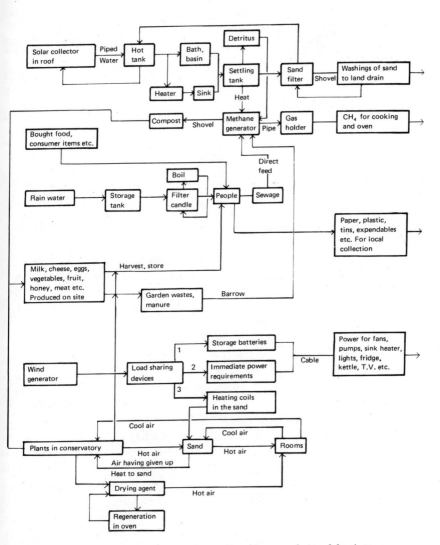

110 A simple low-energy system, with recycling of wastes, designed for Autonomous House 1.

References

2 Power from the sun

ANDERSON, B. (1973): *Solar Energy and Shelter.* Thesis for Master of Architecture at Massachusetts Institute of Technology.

ANON. (1973): 'The sun breaks through as an energy source' in *Business Week*, 19 May. McGraw-Hill, New York.

BAER, S. (1973): 'Solar house' in *Alternative Sources of Energy* No. 10, March. Minong, Wisconsin.

BOER, K.W. (1973): 'The solar house and its portent' in *Chemtech, the innovator's magazine*, July.

CLAYTON, W.P. (1966): *Notes on the new St. George's Secondary School.* Issued by the County Borough of Wallasey, Cheshire.

DANIELS, F. (1964): *Direct Use of the Sun's Energy.* Yale University Press.

DANIELS, F., and J.A. Duffie (eds.) (1955): *Solar Energy Research.* Thames and Hudson, London.

DAVIES, G.M., N.S. Sturrock and A.C. Benson (1971): 'Some results of measurements on St. George's School, Wallasey' in *Journal of the Institution of Heating and Ventilating Engineers*, July, Vol. 13, pp. 77–84.

HAY, H. (1969): 'International aspects of air conditioning with movable insulation' in *Solar Energy*, Vol. 12, pp. 427–38.

HOTTEL, H.C., and B.B. Woertz (1942): 'The performance of flat-plate solar heat collectors' in *Proceedings of the American Society of Mechanical Engineers*, Feb.

HEYWOOD, H. (1954): 'Solar energy for water and space heating' in *Journal of the Institute of Fuel*, July.

LEARMOUTH, R.A. (1973): 'Solar heated houses are nearing reality in the USA' in *Heating and Ventilating Engineer*, pp. 123–5.

LORSCH, H.G. (1973): 'The use of solar energy for residential space heating' in *Energy Conversion*, Vol. 13, pp. 1–5. Pergamon Press, Oxford.

LOUDON, J.C. (1817): *Remarks on the Construction of Hot Houses.* London.

MARKUS, T. (1964): 'Skill – solar energy and building design' in *The Architectural Review*, June, pp. 456–62, and July, pp. 68–96.

MOORCROFT, C. (1973): 'Solar energy in housing' in *Architectural Design*, No. 10. London.

Proceedings of the United Nations Conference on New Sources of Energy (1961): section on solar houses.

Proceedings of the Conference on Applied Solar Energy at Phoenix, Arizona (1956).

ROUVIER, A. (1973): 'Les vitrages réfléchissants, éléments d'esthétique et de confort dans l'habitat'. Conference Paper EH79 delivered at conference on 'The Sun in the Service of Mankind', Paris, July.

SMITH, G. (1973): 'Air conditioning with sun and outer space' in *Alternative Sources of Energy*, No. 10, March. Minong, Wisconsin.

THOMASON, H.E. (1972): *Solar Houses and Solar House Models*. Edmund Scientific Co., Barrington, N.J.

TROMBE, A.F., and J. Michel (1973): *Maison Sept.* Frazier, Paris.

WHILLIER, A. (1964): *Notes on solar energy*. Technical report no. T63, Brace Research Institute, Macdonald College of McGill University, Montreal, Canada.

ZAREM, A.M. (ed.) (1963): *Introduction to the Utilization of Solar Energy*. McGraw-Hill, New York.

3   Harnessing the wind

BOSSEL, H. (1970): *Low-cost windmills for developing nations*. Prepared for VITA (Volunteers for International Technical Assistance Inc.), College Campus, Schenectady, New York 12308.

CLEWS, H.M. (1973): *Electric Power from the Wind*. Solar Wind Co., R.F.D.2, East Holden, Maine 04429.

GOLDING, E.W. (1955): *The Generation of Electricity by Wind Power*. Spon, London.

– (1948): *Windmills for water lifting and the generation of electricity on the farm*. Informal Working Bulletin No. 17, Agricultural Engineering Branch, Land and Water Development Division, Food and Agriculture Organisation of the United Nations.

– (1955): 'Electrical energy from the wind' in *Proceedings of the Institute of Electrical Engineers*, Vol. 102, Part A, No. 6, Dec., pp. 677–95.

GOLDING, E. W., and A. H. Stodhart (1949): *The Potentialities of Wind Power for Electricity Generation (with special reference to small-scale operations)*. ERA Technical Report W/T 16.

HUETTER, U. (ed.) (1961): *Proceedings of the United Nations Conference on New Sources of Energy*. Rome.

JOPP, M. (1972): 'Energy from the winds' in *United Power News*. United Power Association, Elk River, Minnesota 55330.

KIDD, S., and D. Carr (1972): 'Can we harness pollution-free electric power from windmills?' in *Popular Science*, Nov., pp. 70–2.

ORTEGA, A., *et al.* (1972): *The Ecol Operation*. McGill University, Montreal, Canada.

PUTNAM, P.C. (1948): *Power from the Wind*. Van Nostrand, New York.

SAVONIUS, S.J. (1931): 'The S-rotor and its application' in *Mechanical Engineering*, Vol. 53, No. 5, May.

SMITH, G. (1973): *The economics of solar collectors, heat pumps and wind generators*. Working Paper 3 (April), University of Cambridge, Department of Architecture.

SOUTH, P., and R.S. Rangi (1971): 'Preliminary tests of a high-speed vertical-axis windmill model'. NRCC (National Research Council of Canada) Laboratory Technical Report LTR–LA–74, March.

– (1972): 'A wind-tunnel investigation of a 14′-diameter vertical-axis windmill'. NRCC Laboratory Technical Report LTR–LA–105, Sept.

STEADMAN, P. (1973): Private (unpublished) report to Pennsylvanian Academy of Natural Sciences.

SWEENEY, T.E. (1973): *The Princeton Windmill Program*. AMS Report No. 1093 (March), Princeton University Department of Aerospace and Mechanical Sciences.

4   Heat pumps

ANON. (1960): 'Heat pump house' in *Engineering*, 9 Dec., p. 812.

ANON. (1960): 'Domestic heat pump' in *Electrical Review*, 25 Nov.

ANON. (1961): 'Domestic and commercial heat pumps' in *Electrical Review*, 16 June, p. 1086.

ANON. (1972): *How Things Work: the universal encyclopaedia of machines*. Paladin, London.

CURTIS, E.J.W., and M. Komedera (1956): 'The heat pump' in *Architectural Design*, June. London.

CURTIS, E.J.W. (1973): 'Solar house at Rickmansworth, Hertfordshire' in *Architectural Design*, Jan. London.

FABER, O. (1946): 'The value of heat with special reference to the heat pump' in *Proceedings of the Institute of Mechanical Engineers*, Vol. 154, pp. 144–63.

GRIFFITHS, M.V. (1956): 'Some aspects of heat pump operation in Great Britain' in *Proceedings of the Institute of Electrical Engineers*, Dec., pp. 262–78.

KELL, J.R., and P.L. Martin (1963): 'The Nuffield College heat pump' in *Journal of the Institution of Heating and Ventilating Engineers*, Jan., pp. 333–56.

KEMLER, E.N., and S. Oglesby (1950): *Heat Pump Applications*. McGraw-Hill, New York.

NEWALL, A.J. (1973): *Residential Heat Pump Application in Great Britain*. Report by the Electricity Council, Capenhurst, Cheshire.

SMITH, G. (1973): *Economics of solar collectors, heat pumps and wind generators*. Working Paper 3 (April), University of Cambridge, Department of Architecture, Technical Research Division.

VALE, R. (1973): *Services for an autonomous research community in Wales*. Working Paper 5 (June), University of Cambridge, Department of Architecture, Technical Research Division.

5 Recycling waste

ACHARYA, C.N. (1956): 'Your home needs a gas plant' in *Indian Farming*, Vol. 6.

ANON. (1952): 'The utilization of crop wastes' in *International Sugar Journal* 54, p. 321.

BATE, H. (1971): *Methane Gas Production*. Copies available from author at Penny Rowden, Blackawton, Totnes, Devon, England.

BELL, Boulter, Dunlop and Keiller (1973): *Methane, the Fuel of the Future*. Whole Earth Tools, Cambridge, England.

BOHN, H.L. (1971): 'A clean new gas' in *Environment*, Vol. 13, No. 10.

BOSHOFF, W.H. (n.d.): 'The application of methane installations in the tropics'. Faculty of Agriculture, Makerere University, Kampala, Uganda.

CAINE, G. (1973): 'A revolutionary structure' in *Street Farmer*, No. 2, London.

FRY, L.J., and R. Merrill (1973): *New Alchemy Institute News Letter*, No. 3. Santa Barbara, Cal., USA.

GOTAAS, H.B. (1956): *Composting*. World Health Organization Monograph Series.

HOLLAENDER, A., *et al.* (1972): *An Inquiry into Biological Energy Conversion*. University of Tennessee, Knoxville.

The Hutchinson Methane Plants. Tunnel Co. Ltd, Fort Ternan, Kenya.

KLEIN, L. (1959): *River Pollution*, Vol. 3. Butterworth, London.

Mother Earth News (1972): 'Design of the Mother digester'. No. 18, Nov., pp. 7–13. Madison, Ohio.

– (1971): 'Gobar gas'. No. 12, Nov., pp. 28–31. Madison, Ohio.

ROSENBURG, G. (1951): 'Methane production from farm wastes as a source of tractor fuel'. A paper read to the Institute of British Agricultural Engineers, 13 Nov.

SINGH, R.B. (1971): *Bio-gas Plant and its Potential.*

– (1971): *Some Experiments with Bio-gas.*

– (1971): *Bio-gas Plant: generating methane from organic wastes*
All published by the Gobar Gas Research Station, Ajitmal, Etawah, Uttar Pradesh, India.

SMITH, G. (1973): *Economics of water collection and waste recycling.* Working Paper 6 (July), University of Cambridge, Department of Architecture, Technical Research Division.

VALE, B. (1972): *The Autonomous House.* Dissertation 2, July, University of Cambridge, Department of Architecture, Technical Research Division.

6   The problem of water

BOYER, J.A. (1933): *Bulletin of Textile Engineering Station*, No. 2.

COMMITTEE ON RESOURCES AND MAN (1969): *Resources and Man.* W.H. Freeman & Co., Reading, Berks.

DANIEL, E. R., and J. E. Garton (1969): 'An automated upflow filter for domestic water supplies' in *Transactions of the American Society of Agricultural Engineers.*

DEPARTMENT OF THE ENVIRONMENT (1972): *Sinews for Survival.* HM Stationery Office.

GOODIN, F. G., and J. Downing (1959): *Domestic Sanitation.* Estates Gazette Ltd., London.

HILLS, L. (1971): *Grow Your Own Fruit and Vegetables.* Faber & Faber, London.

MOORCROFT, C. (1972): 'Designing for survival' in *Architectural Design*, London, July, pp. 414–45.

Mother Earth News (1972): Reprint from old farm magazines. No. 18, Nov. Madison, Ohio.

NATURAL RESOURCES RESEARCH (1968): *Use and Conservation of the Biosphere.* UNESCO, Paris.

ORTEGA, A., *et al.* (1972): 'The problem is No. 2' in *The Ecol Operation.* Minimum cost housing group, School of Architecture, McGill University, Montreal, Canada.

PIKE, A. (1966): 'Product analysis – basins and bidets' in *Architectural Design*, Jan. London.

– (1966): 'Product analysis – baths', *ibid.*, Feb.

PRETORIUS, W.A. (1971): 'Anaerobic digestion of raw sewage' in *Water Research*, Vol. 5, No. 9, pp. 681–7. Pergamon Press, Oxford.

SEARLE, S. (1970): see 'Bathtime flower power' in *Sunday Times Business News*, London, 12 April.

SMITH, G. (1973): *Economics of water collection and waste recycling.* Working Paper 6 (July), University of Cambridge, Department of Architecture, Technical Research Division.

SZYMANOWSKI, H.W. (1972): *Homelab: integration of new concepts for the living unit.* Paper read at conference on 'Environmental Design: Research and Practice', University of California at Los Angeles, Jan.

VALE, B. (1972): *The Autonomous House.* Dissertation 2, July, University of Cambridge, Department of Architecture, Technical Research Division.

VITA (Volunteers for International Technical Assistance Inc.) (1970): *Village Technology Handbook.* College Campus, Schenectady, New York 12308.

WAGNER, E.G., and J.N. Lanoix (1959): *Water Supply in Rural Areas.* World Health Organization Monograph Series.

WALLMAN, H. (1972): 'Should we recycle/conserve household water?' Paper read at 6th International Quality Symposium, Washington, DC, 18–19 April.

·7   Batteries and fuel cells

ANDREW, M.R., *et al.* (1972): 'A fuel-cell/lead-acid battery hybrid car'. *Society of Automotive Engineers Inc.*, 2 Pennsylvania Plaza, New York, NY 10001.

ANON. (1964): 'Pioneering and perfection at Harrods' in *Electric vehicles*, June, pp. 11–12.

BACON, F.T. (1969): 'Fuel cells, past, present and future' in *Electrochimica Acta*, Vol. 14, pp. 569–85. Pergamon Press, Oxford.

– (1954): 'Fuel cells' in *The Engineer*, Vol. 198.

– (1965): 'Fuel cells' in *Journal of the Institute of Fuel*, September.

BACON, F.T., and T. Fry (1972): 'When there's no more oil and gas' in *New Scientist*, 10 August, pp. 285–7.

BARAK, M. (1970): 'Batteries and fuel cells' in *Institute of Electrical Engineers Reviews*, Vol. 117, August, pp. 1561–84.

BOLL, R.H., and R.K. Bhada (1968): 'Economics of on-site power

generation by fuel cells' in *Energy Conversion*, Vol. 8, pp. 3–18.
Pergamon Press.

GREGORY, D.P. (1973): 'The hydrogen economy' in *Scientific American*, January, Vol. 228 No. 1, pp. 13–21.

HART, A.B., and G.J. Womack (1967): *Fuel cells – Theory and Application*. Chapman and Hall, London.

HEATLIE-JACKSON, D. (1971): 'Plastic/glass tubular design brings advances in stationary batteries' in *Electrical Review*, 18 June.

MITCHELL, W. (1963): *Fuel cells*. Academic Press, New York.

ORLOFSKY, S. (1971): 'Development of a 12.5 kw natural gas fuel cell'. Paper from the Eighth World Energy Conference, Bucharest, 28 June–2 July.

POLE, N. (1973): *Oil and the future of personal mobility*. A Cambridge University Conservation Society Report.

RAMAKUMAR, R., *et al.* (1967): 'A wind energy storage and conversion system for use in underdeveloped countries'. School of Electrical Engineering, Oklahoma State University, Stillwater, Oklahoma 74074.

SMITH, G. (1973): *Economics of solar collectors, heat pumps and wind generators*. Working Paper 3 (April), University of Cambridge, Department of Architecture, Technical Research Division.

SUMMERS, C.M. (1971): 'The conversion of energy' in *Scientific American*, September, pp. 149–60.

VIELSTICH, W. (1970): *Fuel cells*. Wiley, New York.

YOUNG, G.J. (1960): *Fuel cells*. American Chemical Society, New York.

8 Storing heat

ALLCUT, E.A., and F.C. Hooper (1961): 'Solar energy in Canada' in *Proceedings of Conference on New Sources of Energy*, Vol. 4, S/20, pp. 304–9. United Nations.

BAER, S. (1973): 'Solar house' in *Alternative Sources of Energy*, No. 10, March. Minong, Wisconsin.

BUCHBERG, H., and J.R. Roulet (1968): 'Simulation and optimisation of solar collection and storage for house heating' in *Solar Energy*, Vol. 12, pp. 31–50. Pergamon Press, Oxford.

DANIELS, F. (1964): *Direct Use of the Sun's Energy*. Yale University Press.

DANIELS, F., and J.A. Duffie (eds.) (1955): *Solar Energy Research*. Thames and Hudson, London.

DUDLEY, J.C. (1972): *Thermal energy storage unit for air-conditioning systems using phase-change material*. University of Pennsylvania, Report No. NSF/RANN/SE/G127976/TR72/8.

GOLDSTEIN, M. (1961): 'Some physical and chemical aspects of heat storage' in *Proceedings of Conference on New Sources of Energy*, Vol. 5, pp. 411–17. United Nations.

HOTTEL, H.C. (1955): 'Residential uses of solar energy' in *Proceedings of the World Symposium on applied solar energy*. Menlo Park, California.

IHVE (1970): *IHVE Guide Books A, B and C*. Curwen Press, London.

SPEYER, E. (1961): 'Solar buildings in temperate and tropical climates' in *Proceedings of Conference on New Sources of Energy*. United Nations.

THOMASON, H.E. (1972): *Solar Houses and Solar House Models*. Edmund Scientific Co., Barrington, N.J.

TYBOUT, R.A., and G.O.G. Löf (1970): 'Solar house heating' in *Solar Energy*, Vol. 14, No. 3, pp. 253–77. Pergamon Press, Oxford.

WHILLIER, A. (1964): 'Notes on solar energy'. *Technical Report No. T63*, Brace Research Institute, Macdonald College of McGill University, Ste. Anne de Bellevue 800, Quebec, Canada.

YEH, H. (1973): *Conversion and better utilisation of electric power by means of thermal energy storage and solar heating*. Phase III, Progress Report No. NSF/RANN/SE/G127976/PR73/1.

ZAREM, A.M. (ed.) (1963): *Introduction to the Utilisation of Solar Energy*. McGraw-Hill, New York.

Index